#460

VHF HAM
RADIO
HANDBOOK

By Edward G. MacKinnon

TAB BOOKS
BLUE RIDGE SUMMIT, PA.

FIRST EDITION

FIRST PRINTING—APRIL 1968

Library of Congress Card Number: 68-21591

Contents

Preface

Do you remember 1934? Well, if you were a ham then, you'll surely never forget how hard it was to get a 10-meter rig on the air! Coaxial cable was not widely available then, and it was hard to find a receiver that would stay put on frequency.

How times have changed!

Here we are talking about parametric amplifiers, tunnel diodes, UHF transistors, low-noise tubes, voltage-tuned capacitors and whatnot! Little did we think twenty years ago that many of us would be playing around with 400-MHz gear and taking 6 and 2 meter operations for granted! And now, with the strides that have been made and are being continued in space communications and telemetering equipment, we are entering a new era—an era of VHF and UHF spectrum exploitation.

Every so often we hear screams of brother hams (including me) on the subject of low-frequency ham band cuts. But if we stop to think of what has not been done on our allocated VHF and UHF bands, there is reason to blush. It is true that our Armed Services "spark-plugged" the development and use of VHF and UHF gear. The contributions made in the radar field alone have certainly advanced the state of the VHF-UHF art years ahead of its time. But we hams (most of us, anyway) who are interested in progress—technical progress—realize that the pioneering spirit must again become a part of our existence. We cannot be content to continue to work on the 10, 15, 20, 40, and 80 meter bands. We must "break out" in force and attempt to use our VHF and UHF spectrum. Maybe we will need a few fixed relay stations here and there; some new antenna arrays, etc., but I am sure that as time goes on we will find a way to use and enjoy VHF and UHF communications over distances undreamed of today.

The future of VHF and UHF, as far as I am concerned, is very bright. If we hams can learn to profit by the advancements being made by our armed services and various research and development agencies in aerospace communications, we certainly will "bust" out of our shells as we did when we began using the 10 meter band. In order to be able to do something about the VHF-UHF situation, we cannot afford to be afraid of experimentation with the new. We must, like Frank Jones (W6AJF), dig into our present resources and try the untried. Only in this manner can we make some good solid contributions to the science of amateur radio—in the VHF and UHF fields.

Are you on 6, 2, and 220? You're not? Well, I suggest you try them—maybe you'll only work across town—but the day will come when you will be using these bands as we now use 10, 15, and 20 meters. Oh yes, there have been some nice DX contacts on 2 meters, but too few. Remember—it takes two to QSO on any band, but it only takes one to come up with a new piece of VHF or UHF gear that will enable better and more consistent QSOs. Design, build, and rebuild! I seriously believe that the higher frequency bands will eventually prove to be the ham's real communications salvation.

The author wishes to thank the following VHF men (listed here by call letters) for their contributions to this work: K1AII, K1CYW, K1CXV, K1HTK, W2AZL, WA2CLT, WA2CWA, WA2DEW, K2DQT, WA2GBW, W2GKR, K2HAK, K2HFL, K2IAP, W2IBD, K2RIH, K2RRG, W2SHU, W2TQS, K2UTN, K2UYH, W3FEY, W3HFY, K3HNP, W4DYE, K4ZAD, WA6CHJ, W6MMU, W6QLV, W6RJJ, K6RNQ, K8REG, K9SRW, LU3DCA, and VE7AIZ.

Edward MacKinnon

CHAPTER 1
VHF Hints and Kinks

The successful operation of VHF equipment depends upon the degree of integration between the mechanical and electrical design of the circuit. Great emphasis must be placed on component placement, since the interplay between electrical and mechanical considerations has as much effect upon the performance of a VHF unit as does the electrical value of the most critical components.

The Wavelength Factor

At frequencies below about 30 MHz, small lengths of wire may be employed as interconnections between parts of an RF circuit and normally cause no trouble, since these bits of copper are short when compared to the wavelength at which the equipment is used. At VHF, however, the normal physical dimensions of coils, capacitors, tubes, leads, chassis — all the parts that go to make up VHF units — begin to approach a large fraction of the wavelength of the frequency at which it is used. Even the electron becomes relatively cumbersome, as the minute time it takes to pass from cathode to plate in the vacuum tube becomes an appreciable part of the radio cycle. A metal chassis can no longer be thought of as a fixed point of ground reference, since points of maximum voltage and current may be found along the surface. Metal enclosures may exhibit peculiar characteristics as they cease to be a shield and become resonant cavities. Short wires, normally docile at lower frequencies, can turn into radiating antennas that couple VHF energy into adjacent circuitry. Coils may act as capacitors; capacitors as coils; or perhaps cease to function at all. As the operating frequency is raised, common vacuum tubes lose their efficiency bit by bit until at some critical frequency they cease to function, paralyzed by the minute time lag of electron passage.

VHF Techniques

As the physical size (wavelength) of the radio wave decreases, the size of the components handling this wave must also decrease so that a rough state of equilibrum is maintained between the two. A twilight region is finally reached, bordering upon the UHF portion of the spectrum, wherein modified low-frequency techniques must be rejected entirely in favor of new concepts in wave motion and equipment design.

Vacuum Tube Limitations

A combination of crippling factors present in the common vacuum tube tend to diminish the efficiency of the tube as the

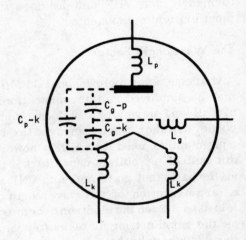

Fig. 1-1. Common triode tube schematic exhibiting several limitations to be considered at VHF frequencies.

operating frequency is raised. In old style tubes a noticeable decline in operation may be observed as low as 20 or 30 MHz. Some common tubes of improved design function well at 150 MHz or so, and others operate at 500 MHz and higher. Tubes operating in the UHF region bear little or no resemblance to their low-frequency counterparts.

At very high frequencies the common triode tube (Fig. 1-1) must be viewed as an AC circuit element having capacities Cg & Cp, Cg & Ck, and Cp-k, and inductances Lp, Lg, and Lk which are inherent in the structure of the tube. These values exist because the tube must have finite size, and must have sufficient lead lengths to permit connection to the circuit

8

components. All of these internal parameters have an important effect upon the operation of the tube. At low frequencies the external circuit capacitances and inductances are large in value compared to those of the tube, and the capacitance of the internal parameters is negligible. As the operating frequency of the tube is raised, interelectrode capacitances become a proportionately greater fraction of the total circuit capacitance. At the same time, the inductance of tube leads becomes increasingly important. A point is finally reached where the total resonant circuit may be expressed in terms of the residual parameters of the tube. This condition is termed the "self-resonant frequency" of the tube.

The inductance of a short tube lead may be surprisingly high in the VHF region. For example, a lead 4 inches long and .04 inches in diameter has an inductance of about 0.1 microhenry. At 1000 KHz the impedance of this lead is only 0.63 ohm. At a frequency of 100 MHz, however, the impedance of this short bit of wire is 63 ohms, since impedance is directly proportional to the frequency. An impedance of 0.63 ohms may have no effect upon circuit operation at 1000 kHz, but an impedance of 63 ohms at 100 MHz may very well cause a VHF circuit to cease functioning. To reduce the impedance to the value obtained at 1,000 kHz, the wire must be reduced in length to less than one-half inch.

Lead Inductance

The inductance of the grid lead of a vacuum tube tends to reduce the signal voltage reaching the grid of the tube, as compared to the voltage impressed at the grid terminal. This reduction becomes more prominent as the frequency of operation is raised. Cathode lead inductance furnishes a common impedance between the grid and plate circuits, introducing undesired coupling. Plate lead inductance acts to reduce the output signal voltage of the tube. The upper limit of operation of the common vacuum tube is somewhat lower than the self-resonant frequency of the elements, since this limit is also a function of the input loading, the transit time, and the resonant frequency of the L-C circuit.

Lead inductances may be reduced by the use of short, heavy tube leads. In some VHF tubes, multiple leads are employed to further drop lead inductance. Tube elements are mounted

9

close to the glass seal, and in some cases the tube pins are gold plated to reduce the effects of atmospheric corrosion.

Electron Transit Time

Under conditions of low-frequency vacuum tube operation, it is usually assumed that electrons leaving the cathode reach the plate of the tube instantaneously. Although nothing in nature happens instantaneously, no harm is done by this assumption as long as the actual time of passage between cathode and plate is negligible compared to the duration of one radio wave. For example, transit time of 1/1000 microsecond (10^{-9} second) is only 1/1000 of a wave at a frequency of 1 MHz. If the same transit time between cathode and plate becomes 1/10 wave or less, it will not permit satisfactory operation of a vacuum tube. At transit times longer than this the tube efficiency drops considerably, and when the transit time approaches a quarter wave the tube will not oscillate.

Circuit Noise

Absolute receiver sensitivity in the very high frequency region is not limited by atmospheric noise as it is at the lower frequencies. Rather, it is a function of the magnitude of circuit noise of the receiver which is composed of antenna noise, input circuit noise, and tube noise.

Circuit noise is masked at the lower frequencies by the high external noise picked up by the antenna. This external noise is composed of atmospheric noise generated by static electricity, cosmic noise received from outer space, and various kinds and intensities of man-made noise. The level of external noise seems to drop off gradually at higher frequencies until in the 100 MHz region it is quite low. Circuit noise, on the other hand, is of minor importance until a frequency of 50 or 70 MHz is reached. At this point the external noise level becomes quite low and the circuit noise level becomes a factor. By proper design circuit noise can be reduced to a great degree, permitting reception of extremely weak VHF signals.

Thermal Agitation

In any substance the molecules are always in a state of

random motion. Temperature, in fact, is a measure of this random motion, and it is only at absolute zero (-273° Centigrade) that such motion ceases. As the temperature of the substance rises above absolute zero the random motion of the molecules increases. The motion of the molecules in a conductor varies the instantaneous position of the free electrons of the conductor. This electron agitation corresponds to a minute electrical current flowing in the conductor and is known as "Thermal Agitation Noise," or "Johnson Noise." This noise is a random fluctuation and is generated over a wide band of frequencies. (An analogy may be taken from the study of white light which is composed of all the colors of the spectrum. Random noise is often termed "White Noise.")

Conductors

Soft-drawn, single-strand copper wire or strap is, in general, the best material to employ as a conductor in the VHF portion of the spectrum. Stranded wire may be used where connection to a moving part is required, but the RF loss in such wire is substantially higher than in an equivalent section of solid wire. Because of the skin effect, the higher frequency current tends to concentrate near the surface of the wire, particularly at sharp corners. A round conductor, therefore, provides the best balance of current concentration. The self-inductance of a single wire at high frequencies is important and this factor must be watched in resonant circuits.

Converter Adjustment

The procedure to be followed in converter adjustment and alignment is essentially the same, regardless of the design of the unit. The first step is to check all wiring for errors before power is applied to the converter. If a grid dip oscillator is handy, the resonant frequency of each tuned circuit should be measured with all the converter tubes in their sockets. Slight adjustments should be made to the coils to bring the circuits to the approximate resonant frequency.

The second step is to adjust the crystal oscillator and doubler stages. A #48 or #49 (2-volt, 60 ma) pilot lamp with a 1-inch diameter loop of wire soldered to base terminals is held near the oscillator coil, and the tuning capacitor adjusted until the lamp glows. A sluggish crystal may require a turn or two added to the feedback coil to sustain oscillation. Excessive feedback will be noticed as variations in lamp brilliancy, or as "birdies" heard in the station receiver when the latter is attached to the converter.

The third step is to adjust the coupling between the various stages of the converter for optimum noise figure. The first adjustment to make is the antenna coupling circuit. The antenna tap on the RF coil, or the antenna link coil, should be varied for best N/F. If a cascode amplifier is used, the filament circuit should be opened and the neutralizing coil adjusted for minumum signal leakage when a signal is applied to the antenna circuit. The second step is to adjust the coupling between the RF amplifier and the following stage. Too much coupling will result in spurious signals, while too little coupling will result in a deterioration of the noise figure. Coupling capacitors should be tapped along the inductances to obtain the best value of N/F.

The final step is to adjust the level of oscillator voltage injection. This may be done by varying the oscillator-mixer coupling capacitor, or by changing the degree of coupling between the injection coils if inductive injection is employed. In some instances the N/F may be materially improved by hand-selecting the tube employed in the first RF stage. The final check is to measure all tube electrode voltages to make sure that they are operating within specifications set by the manufacturer.

A Few Random Hints

Carbon Mike RF Problems: When using carbon mikes, I have been troubled with RF getting into the mike button and causing feedback, even though shielded cable was used on it. Bypassing the mike with a .001-μμf ceramic capacitor right at the terminals of the mike button will eliminate this annoyance. This wrinkle has worked on at least three 522 rigs.

SCR-522 Remote Metering: An electric razor cord, or a TV cheater cord with the side mounts cut off, will fit the meter plug on the 522 transmitter for remote metering.

Surplus Relays for Switching: I use 12- and 24-volt surplus relays in most of the equipment here. As most of these relays close at between 50 and 100 ma, adjust the variable resistor as shown in Fig. 1-2 to obtain this amount of current. I use this circuit in all transmitters. It also is used for antenna switching and receiver muting, and has been used successfully on the DX100 transmitter, too.

Carbon Mike on Crystal Inputs: If you would like to use a carbon mike on a transmitter with crystal input, the circuit in Fig. 1-3 is easy to use and has worked well for me. This circuit has a little more output than a crystal mike when used with a 3-volt battery. The values shown are not critical and may be modified to fit your gear.

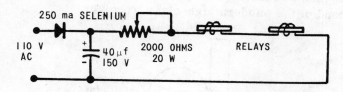

Fig. 1-2. Switching circuit using "surplus" relays.

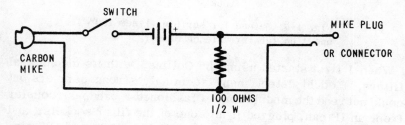

Fig. 1-3. Carbon mike adapter circuit for use with a crystal input.

Aligning Yagi Beam Elements: Anyone who has ever attempted to build a VHF beam has probably run into one problem or another that seemed almost insuperable. Here is one of those problems which I ran into and was able to solve. The problem is to get all the elements of the beam in a straight line. In order to do this you must scribe two lines on opposite sides of the boom and keep them exactly 180° apart. To do this, place the boom on the floor and secure one end to prevent rolling. Now, place a square flush against the floor and against the boom. By sliding the square along the boom you find that a line has been scribed along the side at the dia-

meter of the boom. By repeating this procedure on the opposite side you will get two lines exactly 180° apart. See
Fig. 1-4.

Boosting AM Reception on Highly-Sensitive Receivers: "Ya
gotta hear 'em to work 'em." That is probably the most
often quoted bromide in Hamdom. But nowadays, what one
wants to hear will govern the choice of receiving equipment
and the technique used. It may come as a surprise to some,
but a highly selective receiver (even a high signal/noise ratio)
is not the best setup for reception of weak AM signals. The
reason is very simple. Those voice frequencies which con-
tribute most to intelligibility will fall completely outside the
passband of the modern high-class receiver.

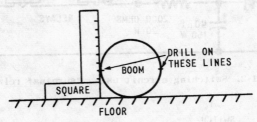

Fig. 1-4. Method for scribing lines 180°
apart on tubular antenna member.

When I first started using the Collins, with its mechanical
filters, I could detect many seemingly strong carriers but
could not read the modulation. I fashioned a bandpass coupler
from an IF can, plugged it into one of the filter sockets, and
presto! Those carriers became Q5 signals. SSB and CW signals are just the opposite. A very narrow passband is very
desirable. A sideband signal is almost impossible to hold
under conditions of violent QSB. On many openings last
Spring, I found it impossible to complete a QSO with SSB stations. It appeared that a 500- or 600-watt SSB station was
about equal to a good 50-watt AM station. It is probably best
summed up by a remark made to me by K6PYH (on SSB):
"At least, it gets you out of the Gooney Boxes."

CHAPTER 2

VHF Propagation Techniques

The use of CW is important to the serious VHF amateur. Certain modes of VHF propagation are almost the exclusive domain of the CW operator. These modes include meteor scatter, moonbounce, and aurora communications. This is because CW is more effective in weak signal communications. It is generally recognized that there is a 17 db advantage of CW over AM in communication circuits. That's a power ratio of 50, which means a 20-watt CW station should be able to do as well as a one KW AM transmitter, all other things being equal. Looked at differently, it takes a large increase in the number of elements in your beam before you can realize a 17 db increase in gain. Even neglecting the more exotic forms of VHF propagation, CW will certainly allow you to extend your groundwave range no matter how large your present antenna is or how much power you now employ.

From a practical standpoint, everyone recognizes that very little CW is actually employed on the VHF bands. This appears to be due to several factors, none of which should be valid in view of the power advantage offered by CW. The biggest factor probably is that the VHF bands are populated mostly by Technician Class operators with slow-speed CW ability who find this mode of operation difficult. CW is an art that can be best mastered by practice, and undoubtedly the best form of practice is attempting to copy a message sent during the course of a QSO.

Keying Monitor

Another difficulty that prevents many operators from enjoying CW is the lack of an adequate means of monitoring their keying. Without a monitor it is almost impossible to develop the smooth rhythm that is the mark of a good CW operator.

15

The following is a description of a simple side-tone generator that will produce an audio tone every time your key is depressed. The monitor is a keyed free-running multivibrator. See Fig. 2-1. Since it requires neither transformers or bulky capacitors and is built around a miniature 9-pin tube, the entire circuit can be constructed on a turret socket. Being small in size, it can be tucked into a corner of a piece of your equipment.

The monitor was designed to be keyed in parallel with any cathode-keyed stage of your transmitter. It can be powered

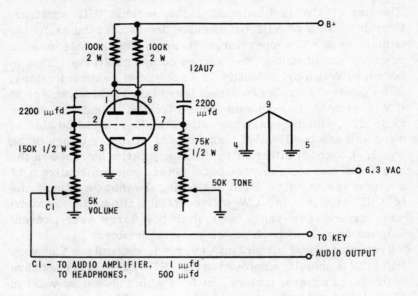

Fig. 2-1. Simple sidetone generator employed as a keying monitor for VHF transmitters.

from any voltage source between 100 and 400 volts available in your rig. Since the drain at 400 volts is only about 5 ma, little additional loading of your power supply will be encountered by its use. A SPST switch placed in the power lead would allow the side-tone to be turned off during phone operation of your transmitter. The use of audio coupling capacitor C1 will depend on whether you feed the side-tone through the audio stages of your receiver or directly to headphones. Most receivers have an auxiliary audio stage input and this is a convenient point to attach the monitor. The tone control is optional, and it and the associated 75K resistor can be replaced by a 150K 1/2 watt resistor. If you don't already own a CW monitor, try building this one. Get on CW, join the fun and work some real VHF DX!

Basic VHF Propagation Phenomena

Before discussing any one propagation type, we should know how and where all the various forms of propagation take place in the atmosphere. This relatively thin layer extends from the earth's surface out (or up) approximately 300 miles. But to say that Sporadic E skip takes place in the earth's atmosphere would be like saying Newark is located in North America. Therefore, we must break down the earth's atmosphere.

Starting from the earth's surface upward to a height of about six miles, we have the troposphere. The next area after leaving the troposphere is known as the stratosphere, a region that extends upward from the troposphere about 30 miles.

We have now broken down the earth's atmosphere into two regions accounting for approximately forty miles of the 300-mile layer. The remaining region above the stratosphere, extending to the edge of the earth's atmosphere, is the ionosphere. Generally speaking, all VHF contacts of over 800 miles are the result of propagation supported by the ionosphere. It accounts for Sporadic E, F2, aurora, and the various types of scatter. I believe in starting at the bottom and working up. So, let's begin with the part of the earth's atmosphere we live in.

Tropospheric Propagation

Tropospheric propagation could be truthfully called tropospheric bending. The change in direction of a radio wave could be illustrated by a comparison with light waves. Let's look back to the time as youngsters when we tried to hit fish in a brook and didn't succeed. We failed not only because of poor aim but also because the fish wasn't where we saw it. The light rays reflected from the fish were bent at the boundary between the water and air; consequently, we saw the fish other than at his true location. In a similar fashion, lenses and prisms bend light waves; therefore, just as light waves may be reflected or bent so also may radio waves.

All of our weather—snow, rain, wind, etc.—is formed in the tropospheric layer. For this reason it is sometimes referred to as the weather layer. The troposphere is of prime importance to the VHF man in that it is where ground-wave propagation takes place. Groundwave, like the weather, is subject to change without notice because the effectiveness of such transmissions are determined solely by the weather.

Even in the most elementary discussions of propagation, it is important we use the correct terminology. The term groundwave is commonly used in referring to contacts made in the absence of skip propagation. We now know that the condition of the VHF bands as far as groundwave coverage is concerned is determined by the weather. The term "ground-wave" is of course a misnomer and probably is a carry-over from low-frequency work; however, the term has come into general use in VHF work to denote an extension of the normal range of transmission and reception to several hundred miles, depending, of course, on frequency. "Groundwave" is a form of tropospheric bending. It is most prevalent in coastal areas, or areas adjacent to large lakes. Again, our weather element.

Have you wondered why one day groundwave signals are very strong, and 24 hours later the same signals are down in the mud? The path between stations hasn't changed, but what has changed is the weather. This is not to say the change was such to be noticed at ground level or as obvious a change as from hot to cold. This change in tropospheric conditions is known as a temperature inversion. There are many types and as many causes of temperature inversions. Perhaps, a general explanation of the causes and results would help the VHF operator to anticipate and thus capitalize on this phenomenon.

Here is a text book definition of a temperature inversion: "When masses of air become stratified into regions having differing dielectric constants." While this statement is absolutely true, perhaps after reading it a newcomer making an honest effort to learn about propagation would be confused, or worse yet, discouraged. What we are trying to understand is why under certain conditions our groundwave coverage is extended beyond its normal range.

The proper term used to describe the result would be tropospheric refraction or tropo bending. Using the proper terminology here is important in that it, in part, tends to define

18

as well as describe this phenomenon. After leaving the antenna, VHF radio waves travel at an angle up through the earth's atmosphere and on into outer space. This is the normal path VHF signals would continue to follow if it were not for propagation. Much like a switch yard reroutes freight cars, various conditions in the earth's atmosphere reroute VHF signals.

A typical example of a temperature inversion would occur if, during a hot spell, a cool front were to move in. The cool air mass moves in and is positioned below a hot air mass. Now we have two layers of air, the lower air mass being cooler is the denser of the two. When the VHF signal enters the cool air mass (at an angle), its speed is slowed down due to the density of the layer. The radio waves traveling at an angle other than 90° will not leave the cool air mass in one part, nor will they enter the less dense hot air mass in one part. The first part of the radio wave to enter the less dense hot air mass is speeded up, causing it to get ahead of the other sections of the wave that will follow later. This sort of pivot action changes the direction in which the radio waves are moving. Instead of continuing off into space, they are bent back toward earth. The extent of this bending is determined by the relative density of the air masses. When the boundary of a temperature inversion is sharply defined, radio waves traveling at low angles of elevation are trapped by the refracting layer of air and will continue to be bent back toward the earth. Radio waves trapped in such a way will follow a duct formed by the boundary layer and the earth's surface. If your antenna is in this tropo duct, groundwave contacts for several hundred miles are possible.

Temperature inversions are more likely to occur during the warmer months of the year. But look for the super inversions during early summer and early fall when slow moving high pressure fronts (cool air), traveling west to east, are met by warm humid masses moving north from the Gulf of Mexico. Stationary fronts can be formed, thereby causing sharp inversions lasting a few days at a time.

Perhaps, now that you have a general picture of a temperature inversion, you can better understand why groundwave is best early in the morning and again after sunset. Remember, we need two air masses of unlike density in order that the speed of a radio wave be changed. At sunrise the upper air is the first to be heated by the sun's rays, while the lower air nearer to the surface of the earth is still cool due to the effects of night. After sunset the reverse is true; without the heat of the sun, the earth cools rapidly, in turn allowing lower atmosphere to cool. Both are forms of temperature inversions resulting in tropo bending.

When discussing VHF groundwave, it would be fair to say that it is the toughest way of getting out. To illustrate this, how many QSL cards do you have confirming skip contacts over one thousand miles away? Now count your groundwave QSLs from stations a mere hundred or two hundred miles away. The ionosphere helped get your signal out to the West Coast. By contrast, to get a good signal to the next state you've got to have help from the troposphere. But, the station set up to get the best possible groundwave coverage will also be best prepared to skip.

The three factors contributing to effective VHF communications are the antenna system, station equipment, and operating skill. The latter factor is a subject in itself. But bear in mind the skillful operator has the ability to anticipate various conditions. Station equipment for effectively working ground-wave should consist of a transmitter of at least medium power capable of A1 and A3 emission. The receiver and converter —the best your means will allow. As for your antenna system, think long and hard before putting up something that may end up being a weak link in an otherwise strong chain. Only by improving the antenna system can your groundwave coverage be extended, both in your ability to receive as well as get out. First you must hear the signals. Many hams stack their VHF antennas without knowing why. True, by doubling the size of the antenna we can realize a gain of 3 db (if stacked correctly). But just as important, if not more so, by stacking the antenna correctly we've lowered the angle of radiation. In groundwave work, the lower the angle of radiation, the better.

The Aurora

The following material, abstracted from three recent papers appearing in The Journal of Geophysical Research, is presented for those who have observed or worked VHF aurora and who may be interested in recent IGY findings concerning this mode of propagation.

Among the most interesting features of aurora-reflected signals are their spectral characteristic which results in the garbling of AM phone and characteristic note of CW signals. It has been shown that CW signals reflected from the aurora have their spectra shifted and spread by as much as 300-900 Hz at frequencies of 50-150 MHz, and as much as 2.5 kHz at operating frequencies of 400 MHz. Fig. 2-2 shows the skip path of a typical transmitted and received (aurora-reflected) signal, illustrating both the Doppler shift and the Doppler spread. The frequency components of the reflected signal fluctuate in amplitude in a noise-like fashion at a rate faster than the response of any spectrum analyzer used to date. The frequency shift may be either up or down, and may pass from one side through zero to a shift in the opposite direction over periods of time as short as one hour.

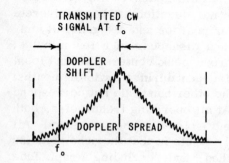

Fig. 2-2. Representation of Doppler shift. See text.

Recent studies by Stanford Research Institute at both Palo Alto, California, and at College, Alaska, on frequencies of 50-400 MHz using antennas of 3° beamwidth with both CW and pulse signals, have shown:

1. That Doppler shift data indicate a predominately east-west motion of the auroral forms. The velocity of motion is 500 meters/sec., and it is independent of time of day.

2. That the magnitude of the Doppler spread on the reflected signal is proportional to frequency over the VHF-UHF range i.e., the spread at 144 MHz is roughly three times that at 50 MHz, and that at 432 MHz is about eight times that at 50 MHz. Thus, received signal distortion becomes progressively worse as frequency is raised. It appears that this

Doppler spread is due to a spectrum of different velocities of individual auroral reflectors in each small volume as would result from small scale turbulence.

3. That the Doppler shift appears to be unrelated to the position in space of the aurora.

4. That the magnitude of Doppler shifts and spreads, for both discrete and diffuse echo returns is similar at a given frequency and is independent of local time.

Using antennas of 3° beamwidth and frequencies from 50 to 800 MHz, the auroral signal returns (echoes) have been characterized as discrete (appearing over only a very narrow range of beam headings). Discrete echoes generally correspond to visual forms of aurora. For these discrete echoes, increasing signal frequency results in decreasing echo amplitude and decreasing average duration. These discrete echoes or reflections drift in position and are generally unstable in that they appear and disappear in a few minutes. Their occurrence shows a broad peak centered around local midnight, and they are most frequent during the winter months.
Diffuse echo returns, on the other hand, do not correspond to anything seen visually. At all operating frequencies, both large layers of reflection and isolated echoes are seen. All diffuse echoes are generally stable in that the echo remains unchanged once it is established, and, excluding a rapid fade rate, the duration of the echo return is long—i.e., in the order of hours. The occurence of these diffuse echoes shows two broad peaks, one centered at 0800 and the other at 1600 local time, while they appear to occur over the entire year in a randomly distributed manner seemingly related to solar activity.
The variations of auroral echo power with operating frequency are poorly understood. For discrete echoes, echo power decreases in direct proportion to an increase in frequency up to about 400 MHz, and then abruptly decreases over a thousandfold for a further doubling of frequency. For diffuse echo returns, echo power decreases as the inverse square of the increase in operating frequency up to at least 800 MHz; i.e., the strength of the echo return at 200 MHz is 1/8 that at 50 MHz, and that at 400 MHz is 1/16 that at 50 MHz.

22

Although many characteristics of auroral signal returns have been defined, important questions remain converning the effect of frequency on the probability of occurrence, the maximum frequency at which auroral propagation can occur (above 800 MHz), and the latitude dependence of auroral propagation.

So much for the scientific status of aurora propagation. However, I would like to add a few pertinent observations drawn from amateur operating experience. The severe distortion of an AM phone signal appears to result largely from the Doppler spread of the carrier, rather than the Doppler spread of the sidebands. Thus, reception of AM signals can often be improved from R1 to R2 or R3 by insertion of a stable carrier with your BFO, using the maximum of received selectivity (i.e., using SSB receiving techniques). Experience by the writer, and many others with SSB, has shown this mode capable of getting through R4 to R5 signals on most 50 MHz auroras when AM signals are unreadable.

Sporadic E Layer Skip

In the E layer region of our atmosphere, at approximately 30 to 70 miles in altitude, clouds of very high ionization frequently are formed. These clouds (not visible, of course) are capable of reflecting VHF signals. It is thought that there is some correlation between aurora and E layer propagation, but this is not definitely known. This cloud layer may be spotty, reflecting signals from a small area or on occasion reaching continental proportions. Propagation by Sporadic E propagation is thought to be limited to (at the highest) 144 MHz and lower; however, 144 MHz transmissions in excess of 1000 miles lead to some question regarding the upper limit. Only in the last few years has any kind of Sporadic E 144 MHz work been possible at all. Minimum distance for Sporadic E skip is about 600 miles and the maximum for single hop is about 1400 miles.

Somewhat related to Sporadic E type is that of F2, which is covered extensively in a later part of this book. Meanwhile, little enough is known about this popular Sporadic layer. It seems that it is best during the months of May, June, and July, but may occur in any month. It appears both during daylight and at night, but tends to peak at about four hours after sunrise and again just after sunset.

"JB," KØRTF, goes about his Sporadic E DX hunting methodically. He keeps a map of the U.S. available at his operating table. When an opening occurs, he may hear a W5 working a W3. A quick check in the callbook locates the W5 in Arkansas and the W3 in Pennsylvania. He draws a line between the location in Arkansas to the point in Pennsylvania. Midway between the two locations on his line he places an X. This is assumed to be the "point of reflection." Soon he has an area giving an idea of the extent of the reflective layer. By locating the "area of reflection" he has been able to work states that he hadn't previously heard by working across this point. The idea is simple and workable. Perhaps you'd like to try it.

Communications on 144 MHz by Aurora Reflection

The largest number of auroras occur in the spring and fall of the year, although one may occur at any time. There are many ways of determining when an aurora is in progress or about to commence. Listen on the lower frequencies, 3.5 through 14 MHz, for hollow sounding signals and the lack of DX. Some of the gang who live in a TV or FM fringe area have an extra antenna pointed north and look for the appearance of stations from long distances. Another help is to take advantage of the CRPL Radio Warning Service, Boulder, Colo. This can be obtained by writing the National Bureau of Standards CRPL Radio Warning Service, Boulder, Colo., and requesting the CRPL-JB forecasts. They are mailed from Boulder each Wednesday with predictions for the following week. Listen to WWV on 2.5, 5.0, or 10.0 MHz at 19 after and 11 before the hour; they give an idea of the present possibilities of an aurora. If WWV is sending W5, U5, or less, look for aurora on 144 MHz. This is not foolproof, however, since the broadcast is changed only every six hours and conditions may change rapidly during that time. If the lower frequency bands drop out due to a "SID" (sudden ionospheric disturbance), look for an aurora approximately 27 hours later. If an aurora is observed, mark the date in your log and look for a recurrence 27 days later, plus or minus a few days.

Possibly one of the least understood parts of communication by auroral reflection is which way to point the beam. The usual practice is to point it in a northerly direction, and this may work for short-haul contacts up to distances of 500 miles or less with a fairly broad beam. The antenna at my station has a 15° beamwidth to the half-power points and the best direction for the W1, W2, VE1, VE2 is slightly east of north. The W8s peak at about 30° west of north and the W9s 30° west of north. The W4s in Virginia and Kentucky peak at 30° west of north and the more southerly W4s peak progressively further toward the west until the beam is almost directly west for Florida. The W5s and southern WØs peak almost due west. In the case of some of the southern stations, it was found possible to improve the signal strength by tilting the beam. It would appear from these observations that if a station in Nebraska wanted to work a station in New Jersey, he would point his beam in a northeasterly direction and the station in New Jersey would point to the northeast. All of the above is pointed out merely to illustrate the fact that one may get auroral reflections from other than a northerly direction, and advantage should be taken of this fact to work stations at longer distances.

Some observations made at this station in the past 12 years may be of help. The best or longest haul contacts are made during a red aurora. This is because the red aurora occurs at a higher elevation than the green or white. The best auroras seem to coincide with a high pressure area centered over or below the Great Lakes region so that most of the country is in a high pressure area. This would suggest that some help is needed from tropospheric bending and scattering. Usually, a good aurora will last for as many as five or six hours without fading. When the aurora fades, don't shut down; it may be back in a few minutes. If not, check the band in half-hour intervals—you may be pleasantly surprised. Usually, if an aurora fades at 8 to 9 PM it will be back around midnight. Auroras have been observed as far south as Florida, so don't think your location is too far south. While some contacts have been made using phone, these are few and far between. Blow the dust off that old brass key and I'll be seeing you on 144 MHz during the next auroral.

Six-Meter Moonbounce

The following material was prepared by Alan Goodaire, VE3BZS/VE7AIZ, of Victoria, B.C., Canada. In it Alan explains an amazing series of experiments with 50-MHz moonbounce and its results. A MUST for anyone interested in state-of-the-art VHF developments.

I have been interested in the idea of amateur communication via moon reflection since I first saw the report of Ross Bateman's (and other's) attempts and successes with 144 MHz in 1953. A while back, Gail Allwine (W7RDY) and I tried some 50 MHz moonbounce tests. Out of about a dozen tries, a half dozen unsuccessful, mostly due to tube failures or ex-

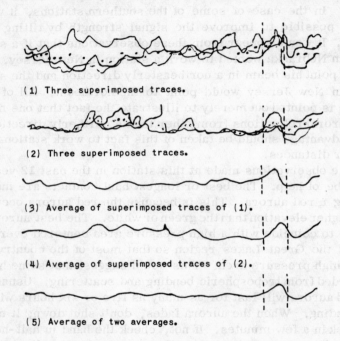

(1) Three superimposed traces.

(2) Three superimposed traces.

(3) Average of superimposed traces of (1).

(4) Average of superimposed traces of (2).

(5) Average of two averages.

Fig. 2-3. Tracings show results of moonbounce tests.

cessive interference (one of these was done by moonset and was just plain unsuccessful). About a half dozen showed some degree of success; Fig. 2-3 shows some of the tracings made from original records. By the way, all tries were done at moonrise, except the one mentioned. Gail ran 800 watts (600 watts approximately into the antenna) into a 4-250A transmitter, keyed automatically to produce 1-second pulses every 15 seconds. The antenna was a 6-over-6 Yagi array.

At VE7AIZ the antenna was a 10-element Yagi. The receiver was at VE7AIZ and consisted of a 6AK5 - 6AK5 - 6J6 converter, with the 6AK5's triode connected and neutralized, with a measured noise figure of just under 3 db at 50 MHz. The station receiver was modified by running the HF oscillator and BFO on batteries to obtain good frequency stability. Also the converter crystal oscillator and buffer stage were run on batteries for the same reason.

The receiver output was passed through an audio filter of about 40-Hz bandwidth, then detected by a germanium diode and the output passed through an R-C filter of a time constant of 1/5 second and displayed on a homemade pen recorder. Receiver tuning was done with a vernier attached to the BFO control after the main tuning control had been roughly set. The BFO was calibrated so the receiver tuning would be corrected for Doppler shift.

The formula arrived at for S/N ratio calculations is:

$$S/N \text{ (a voltage ratio)} = \frac{P_t G_t G_r \eta^2 \times 1.6 \times 10^{-26}}{kT \left[.22\eta^{2.4} + (F\pi = 1)/\eta \right]} =$$

$$\frac{1}{\left(\frac{\eta}{2} B_{3\,db} \frac{1}{4\,RC} \right)^{1/2}}$$

where:

$B_{3\,db}$ is the bandwidth of the tuned circuit (audio filter)

RC is the time constant of the R-C network

P_t is the transmitter output power in watts

G_t is the transmitter gain over an isotropic radiator

G_r is the receiver gain over an isotropic radiator

k is 1.38×10^{-23} joules/degree (Boltzmann's constant)

T is $300°$ Kelvin

$F_{\pi = 1}$ is the noise figure of the tube at $\eta = 1$ meter

27

There are several assumptions made in using the formula, but it gives an idea of what, or rather, why parameters are necessary. This formula assumes, for one thing, that the receiver has a square-law detector and that B_{3db} is quite a bit larger than 1/4RC. The more voltage fluctuates in a random manner, the detection of a signal in the presence of noise becomes more of a statistical problem. One can say very roughly, for example, that this formula should give the S/N ratio within a factor of 2 about 50% of the time, whereas a detection by a factor of 10 is quite unlikely.

One point to be noticed is that for yagis and similar arrays 9η is proportional to the boom length and the optimum wavelength is given by:

$$\eta^{3.4} = 1.9 \ (F_{\pi-1} - 1)$$

for a 416B η optimum = 1/2 meter. However, if a parabolic dish is used, since: $g = \dfrac{4\eta A}{\eta^2}$ and A = area of dish in (meters)^2

$$S/N = \frac{Pt \ (4\eta)^2 \ A^2/\eta^2 \ X \ 1.6 \ X \ 10^{-26}}{kT \left[.22 \ \eta^{2.4} + (F_{\pi-1} - 1)\right] \left[\dfrac{\eta}{2} \ B_{3db} \ \dfrac{1}{4RC}\right]^{1/2}}$$

then the smallest wavelength possible should be used.

I am not positive, but believe also that an extremely narrow beamwidth can be obtained and a tremendous increase in returned signal should be experienced because the problem changes from one in scattering and distance to the fourth-power effect to a distance to the second-power effect.

The echos obtained by the 50-MHz experiments show a retardation by the ionosphere. This is by an amount of, say, 100 times that to be expected by using a simplified formula to calculate this. However, 50 MHz is a bit low for the frequencies the formula is intended to be used at. The delay is about a 10th of a second or so and indicates that a terrific amount of Faraday rotation took place. The MUF was quite close to 50 MHz during most of the experiments, so the ionosphere no doubt had a profound effect on the signal. Because of low S/N ratio, definite conclusions are hard to reach. The

28

S/N of individual echos averaged 1:1, I would say. The formula neglects ground reflection gain and calculated S/N. Without ground reflection, gain was about one half. So probably some of this gain was being realized (if formula correctly describes the situation).

Charting Moonbounce Path Losses

The true moonbounce operator differs from other VHF men because he is looking for a band on which a particular propagation type can be best used, not for a propagation type which can be used best on a certain band. He must make this decision for himself and from incomplete information. Theoretically, he can accomplish moonbounce on any band if he can muster enough gain to overcome the path loss.

The path loss for a moonbounce system can be obtained from the formula:

$$\text{loss in db} = 10 \log 1.62 \times 10^{-26} \times \lambda^2$$

The transmitter used will have a gain according to the formula:

$$Gtx = 10 \log P$$

where:

Gtx is gain in db
P is power output in watts

The gain of most receiving and transmitting antennas can be obtained from various handbooks. The gain of a parabolic antenna, however, is not too frequently seen in amateur publications; it may be determined by the formula:

$$Ga = 10 \log \frac{4\eta \, Rg}{\lambda}$$

where:

Ga is gain in db over an isotropic radiator
R is projected area of reflector in square feet
g is an efficiency factor (approximately 55% for most antennas)
λ is wavelength in meters

Table 2-1. Gains – Pathloss

144 MHz

Antenna Gain	
(64 element beam)	+ 22 db at the transmitter
(64 element beam)	+ 22 db at the receiver
Transmitter Gain	
(750 watts out)	+ 29 db
Receiver Power	
(100-Hz bandwith with	
417A converter)	+ 184 db
Transmission Line Loss	
(transmitter and	
receiver very near antenna)	less than −1 db
Path Loss	−252 db
Total	+ 4 db

432 MHz

Antenna Gain	
(30 ft. dish)	+ 27 db at the transmitter
(30 ft. dish)	+ 27 db at the receiver
Transmitter Gain	
(500 watts out)	+ 17 db

The gain of the receiving system can be obtained by first calculating the power a perfect receiver can achieve from the formula:

PRg = -10 log Kt Δf

where:

PRg is perfect receiver power in db

K   is Boltzmann's constant (1.37×10^{-23})

t   is temperature in °Kelvin

Δf is receiver bandwidth in Hz

30

	Receiver Power (100–Hz bandwidth with preamp)	+ 194 db
	Transmission Line Loss (transmitter and receiver mounted very near or on antenna)	less than −1 db
	Path Loss	−252 db
	Total	+ 19 db
1298 MHz	Antenna Gain (18 ft. dish) (18 ft. dish)	+ 35 db at the transmitter + 35 db at the receiver
	Transmitter Gain (500 watts out)	+ 27 db
	Receiver Power (100–Hz bandwidth with preamp)	+ 105 db
	Transmission Line Loss (Transmitter and receiver mounted on or near antenna)	−1 db
	Path Loss	−271 db
	Total	+ 30 db

From the perfect receiver power, the receiver's noise figure in db must be subtracted to obtain the actual receiver power. It should also be remembered that the transmission line losses must be subtracted from overall gain. Table 2-1 shows theoretical gains -path loss calculated for typical moon-bounce systems on 144 MHz, 432 MHz, and 1298 MHz.

Table 2-1 should not be taken at face value. There are other factors to consider; however, the chart's values do give a starting point from which to work. The big limiting factor not shown on the chart is the Faraday shift. As radio waves travel through the atmosphere their polarization is shifted, thus causing a large db loss due to cross polarization. Although the exact extent of this shift is not known, it is known that the effect is lessened with frequency. The Faraday shift is probably one important reason why practical moon-bounce communications have not been accomplished on the lower VHF bands but has succeeded on 1298 MHz.

Two other factors to be considered in the choosing of a band to try for moonbounce are population and expense. The trend in population seems to be toward 1296, because of recent success on this band. Remembering that one needs a second station for a two-way contact, 1296 seems to be the band to find that second station. The other bands should not be neglected. On 432 the extent of Faraday shift is not known, and it is an easier band to set up a moonbounce system. The 50-watt power limit in effect in certain areas is not so great a deterrent as many believe. With only 50 watts, a system with a favorable gain-loss relationship can be built. The bands above 1298 have great potential with the extremely high antenna gains which can be achieved on them.

CHAPTER 3

VHF Transmitters

Let's go no further until we get a good understanding of what to expect when deviating from the accepted axiom that the shortest distance between two points is a straight line. Anyone considering any piece of VHF gear must bear in mind that lead length, bypassing, etc., is very important to avoid parasitics and instability. If you have sockets which have a center ground post built in, do not use it. Make all ground connections to chassis. The matter of bypassing is very important and in my shack receives very careful attention. The usual disc ceramic used for bypassing here (.001) has a series resonant frequency in the neighborhood of 35 MHz with normal lead length. By shorting the leads together with a copper strap, this frequency can be easily determined with a GDO, and can just as easily be raised to 50 MHz by trimming the lead length. With the series resonant frequency at 50 MHz, an extremely low impedance path to ground is provided for 6 meter RF. Bakelite sockets are not recommended due to RF leakage. Some low value resistors are wirewound, even though they look like composition. Be certain that the ones you use are actually low inductance composition type or you may have to solve the mystery of the exploding resistors as I did!

120 Watts on 6 Meters

The transmitter to be described (Fig. 3-1) came into being as the result of several attempts to pack a lot of power into a small space. After having had many problems with construction and operation, the RF section was put on a normal sized chassis, and with the modulator, plate, and exciter supplies was mounted in a 30" desk top rack.

The circuit consists of a 6CL6 working as a modified Pierce

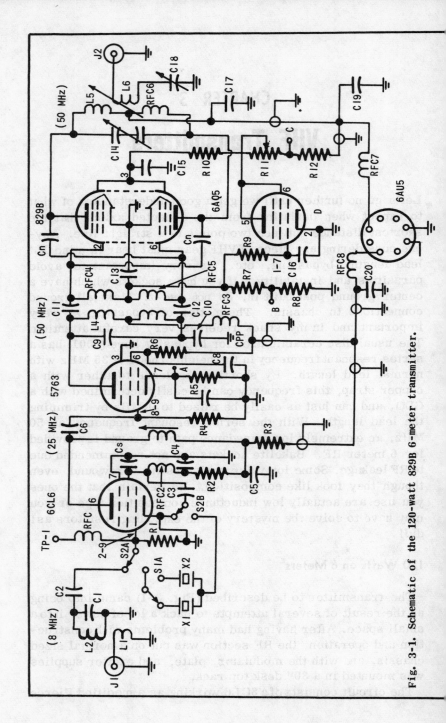

Fig. 3-1. Schematic of the 120-watt 829B 6-meter transmitter.

PARTS LIST

R1	100K
R2	40K
R3	1K
R4	90K
R5, 8, 12	68 ohms
R6	18K
R7	5K, 5 watts
R9	150K
R10	180 ohms
R11	25K, 25W, adjustable

All capacitors .001 600V disc ceramic unless otherwise noted

C1	220 μμf mica
C2	68 μμf mica
C6	50 μμf mica
C9, C18	25 μμf Hammarlund APC
C11, C12	50 μμf mica
C14	15 μμf butterfly Johnson 10LB15
C15	180 μμf button mica
C17, C19	.001, 3KV
CS, CPP, C4	- See text

RFC1, 2	2.5 mh
RFC3, 4	Ohmite Z-50
RFC5, 6	Ohmite Z-50
RFC7, 8	30 turns #28E 1/4" diameter
RFC9	16 turns #16E 1/2" diameter
L1	15 turns #28E close-wound 3/4" diameter
L2	38 turns #28E close-wound 3/4" diameter
L3	12 turns #28E 5/8" long on Nat'l XR-90 form
L4	7 turns #22 7/8" long 3/4" diameter
L5	8 turns #10 1 3/4" long 1" diameter, space at center for L6 - should tune at 2/3 meshed
L6	2 turns #12, 1" diameter
M1	50 ma
S1	SPDT
S2	DP 2 position shorting type (Juggle or squeeze plate until you hit resonance.)
S3	DP 3 position non-shorting type
Filament	wire minimum #16 shielded

oscillator, tripling in the plate circuit and driving a 5763 doubler. The doubler is capacity-coupled to the grids of an 829B or 3E29, which is cross-neutralized and is rock solid. A 5894 may be substituted for either of the above, and it probably would not have to be neutralized. If a 5894 is used, R7 should be changed to 20K, 5 watts. The grid current would be 5 ma and the screen current would be 16 ma. To insure that a loss of drive to the final would not result in a molten pool of glass and metal in the 829B socket, a 6AQ5 is triode-

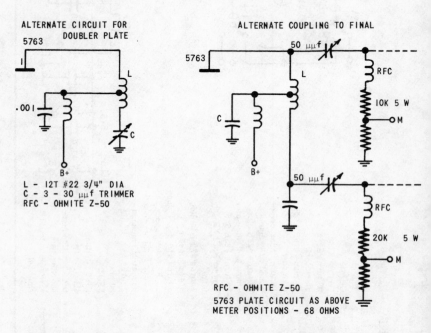

Fig. 3-2. Alternate circuits that can be employed in Fig. 3-1. At left is the alternate circuit for the doubler plate; at right, alternate coupling to the final.

connected as a screen clamp. With no drive, the input to the final is held to a very low value.

Returning to the 6CL6, a tuned circuit can be switched into the grid and any 8-MHz VFO can be used to drive the rig. All power wiring is shielded, and all leads out of the chassis are pi filtered. The cable which connects the RF section to the modulator and power supply sections uses shielded wire and is enclosed in shield braid. The entire rig is enclosed in

Reynolds perforated stock and fastened with a generous number of screws. The meters are shielded, the DC meter with a meter can be fastened to the back of the panel, and the meter leads are shielded and bypassed. The RF meter is covered by a piece of perforated stock.

The transmitter is constructed on a 7" x 15" x 3" chassis, although it could easily be put on a 7" x 10" x 3" with room to spare. I used the larger size so as to have room for 2 meter plate lines. The front panel is a standard 7" x 19" rack panel, secured to the chassis by the various switches and the filament pilot light. The layout of parts is left to the individual, although it is necessary that the layout be such that lead length is kept at a minimum. The final plate tuning capacitor is mounted on a 1/8" x 2" x 2 5/8" poly sheet secured to the chassis by an aluminum angle bracket. Connections to the 829B plates are made with thin copper sheet stock about 1/4-inch wide. Heat dissipating plate connectors should be used to keep the temperature of the plate seals within bounds. I have had great success using Fahnestock clips, although you may wish to use a commercial product such as Bud TC-487. WARNING . . . The rotor of the final plate tank capacitor is not grounded, so it is necessary to use an insulated coupling to bring the control out to the front panel.

The circuitry is straightforward, with two possible exceptions. The oscillator screen may need an additional capacitor to ground, C_s (220 $\mu\mu$f), for fast starting. The doubler plate circuit must be balanced to feed the final grids. If the grid drive is not balanced, the tube (final) will generate harmonics, overheat, and be unstable generally. It may be necessary to place a small trimmer from the lower end of the doubler plate tank to ground to balance the output capacity of the 5763. This is indicated as C_{pp} (3-30 $\mu\mu$f) in Fig. 3-1. In the rig here, it was not necessary due to wiring capacity. WARNING . . . the doubler plate capacitor is at the plate supply potential and must be adjusted with an insulated tool. An alternate circuit is shown to remove that hazard. In the alternate circuit, the coil resonates with the output capacity of the tube and the trimmer to form a balanced plate tank circuit.

The final neutralizing capacitors are made from #12 insulated wire crossed from each grid terminal, through the tube socket, and up the outside of the tube envelope. The wires should protrude at least 3/4" above the chassis at the start.

With full drive and plate and screen voltage applied, the wires should be trimmed EQUALLY, no more than 1/8" at a time, until there is no "kick" in the grid meter as the plate capacitor is tuned through resonance. An alternate method can be used if there is a very sensitive RF detector available. The detector should be loosely coupled to the plate tank, full drive applied, and the plate circuit tuned very carefully to resonance with NO plate or screen voltage applied. The wires would then be trimmed until there is no indication on the detector. In either case, if the neutralizing adjustments are made around 50.25 MHz, they will hold for any frequency normally used for 6-meter operation. I have operated up to 53 MHz and have had perfectly stable operation in all respects.

The circuitry of the 829B is very critical in regard to lead length and little hidden inductances. The cathode should be grounded with a copper strap (a piece of wire does have inductance of 50 MHz). A button mica bypass capacitor is highly recommended for C15, the screen bypass capacitor, and should be mounted as close to the screen terminal as possible. R10 is used to isolate the screen from any stray RF in the power leads. Make sure R10 is non-inductive. The output link is variable and is used to obtain proper loading of the final, along with C18. C18 serves to tune out transmission line reactance and does have a decided effect on loading.

If a single power supply is used for the entire transmitter, a tune-up switch is suggested for the 829B screen circuit. It is not absolutely necessary, since the clamp tube will hold the final input to a safe value, but it is desirable. Power requirements are 400 to 600 volts at 325 ma and 6.3 volts at 4.25 amps. The modulator should be capable of supplying 60 watts without distortion, if you want to run full input. I am modulating with zero-bias Class B 807s, and have a bit of reserve audio.

Operation is as follows: With all tubes in place and the circuits dipped to the operating frequency with a GDO, apply voltage to all but the final screen (if you've put in a tune-up switch, otherwise trust the clamp). The oscillator should start at once and develop 25 to 40 volts negative at TP-1; depending on crystal activity, L3 should be dipped to the proper frequency (approximately 25 MHz) and you should get about 1 ma drive to the 5763. This corresponds to 80 to 90 volts negative at pin 8. Measure this with a 2.5 mh RF choke in series with the voltmeter probe. The doubler tank should dip at 50 MHz with a cathode current of 40 to 45 ma. With the meter in the final grid there should be no difficulty obtaining 15 ma of drive. Under load, 10 to 12 ma is enough. If you have trusted the clamp tube up to this point and have had plate voltage on the final, you should also have had a load connected to the antenna terminal because the final will start to draw plate current as soon as there is enough grid leak bias developed to cut off the clamp tube. With the final loaded so as to draw 200 ma, the screen voltage should be 200 volts and screen current should be 20 ma. DO NOT run the final with a light load or no loading. There is no protection for the screen in the event loading is lost or greatly reduced, and these tubes make very poor triodes.

A note here on the final tank circuit: The circuit without the tube connected will dip to about 80 MHz and will only hit 6 meters with the tube in the circuit. This fact has confused a couple of people when they checked the tank. This rig doesn't have to be given up when the QRO bug bites, since there is adequate output for even the triode kits that have hit the market lately, so it's fine for driving any KW.

Control overdrive to the final can be had by changing R6 to a 25K pot. As long as we're on the subject of things to do, R7 could be removed and a 10K 5-watt resistor placed in series with each final grid RF choke, and each grid could then be metered. Further, C11 and C12 could be replaced by 50-$\mu\mu$f trimmers and grid current could then be very accurately balanced. You would find that C9, C11, and C12 would interact, and a change in one of them would necessitate changing the settings of the other two. With this change in circuitry, grid drive to the final would vary from 5 to 7 ma for each grid.

After the initial tune-up, assuming the antenna is reasonably matched and not too reactive, the only control that need be touched for reasonable frequency changes is the final plate tank. The oscillator plate coil and the doubler are both rather low Q and so cover a rather broad frequency range.

Tripler for 432 MHz

Although activity on the 432-MHz band has risen to a new high lately, there are probably many fellows who have thought about getting started, but have either not known where to begin or

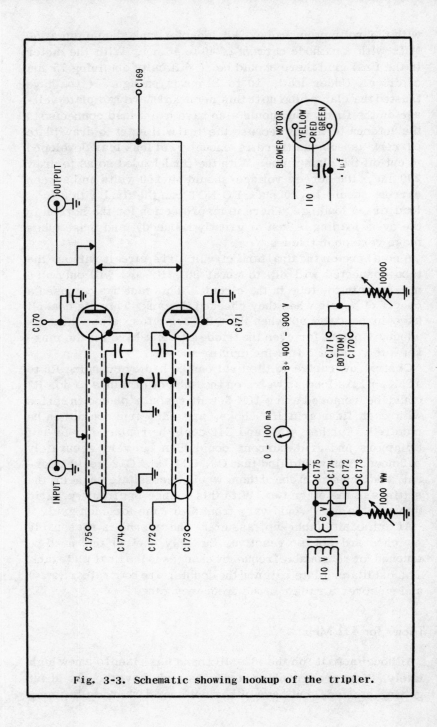

Fig. 3-3. Schematic showing hookup of the tripler.

were wary of investing a chunk of cash in tubes and parts and not being sure of getting results. About the simplest way to get a good 432 signal on the air is to construct a tripler that can be driven by a Gonset Communicator, or any low-powered 144-MHz rig. As far as the transmitter is concerned, the investment is then confined to the parts necessary for the required tripler stage. If constructional know-how or time is limited, you might consider modernizing a piece of surplus gear now available. Although this particular unit is rather large (6 x 6 x 15), sufficient space can probably be found in most hamshacks.

The unit consists of a pair of 2C39s connected in grounded-grid configuration. There is a pair of tuned lines in the cathode (input) circuit, tuned to 144 MHz by a split-stator variable capacitor, and a similar pair is used in the plate (output) circuit, but these are tuned by a slider mechanism. The capacitor and slider are driven by a chain arrangement which most experimenters will prefer to eliminate. The 2C39s are each rated at 100 watts plate dissipation, so they will undoubtedly last a lifetime when operated at the low power level required here. Convection currents to cool the plates would be satisfactory if it weren't for the silver-plated enclosure employed to reduce stray radiation and consequent power loss. Cooling is handled adequately by a 110-volt, 2-phase blower which is supplied with the tripler. The second phase is derived from a 1-mfd paper capacitor. The power supply required is rather flexible. It has been found that output power varies little when the plate supply voltage is varied from 400 to 900 volts. In any case, the total current drain is practically constant at 60-70 ma for all voltages. Grid current is infinitesimal when drive is supplied by a Communicator.

Power output varies from 4 to 7 watts, depending upon many things, including tube condition, plate voltage, tuning adjustments, etc. The biggest variable is the drive power available. If your Gonset is not up to snuff, the tripler will not "talk as loud." If a rig bigger than a Gonset is used, the output will be much greater.

The filament supply voltage is 6 volts at 2 amps. A standard 6.3-volt transformer with small gauge wire to the filaments usually drops the voltage close enough to 6 volts. The filament transformer must not be grounded. A diagram of the hookup is shown in Fig. 3-3.

Tuneup of the tripler is accomplished as follows:

1. Tune up the Communicator to 144.0-144.2 MHz, using a dummy load, or if none is available, to whatever antenna you have.

2. Connect the Communicator to J-113 on the tripler through a length of RG-8/U cable.

3. Set R1 at maximum resistance and R2 at minimum resistance.

4. Turn on the 2C39 filaments and allow 1 minute for warm-up.

5. Turn on the 2C39 plate voltage.

6. Adjust R1 for about 50 ma plate current.

7. Turn the Communicator to TRANSMIT position and tune the input variable capacitor for maximum plate current. As an additional aid, a milliameter may be inserted in series with R2 if necessary. Turn R1 if plate current rises above 70 or 80 ma.

8. Connect an output indicator to J-112. This may be a UHF wattmeter, a 50-ohm resistive load and some sort of diode or VTVM RF probe, or an antenna-field strength meter combination.

9. Tune the output circuit slider until output is indicated. Output will be present when the slider is about 2 1/4 inches from the centerline of the 2C39s.

10. Repeat the adjustments outlined and adjust R1 and R2 and the TUNE and LOAD knobs of the Communicator until no further increase in output can be obtained. Pay no further attention to the plate milliameter for the final adjustments.

It will be found that with plate voltages in the order of 400 volts, R2 will be zero ohms, its optimum value increasing as plate voltage is increased toward 900 volts. Output power will actually decrease with plate voltages above 900 volts. When using the higher plate voltages, enough R1 must be left active to limit the static current to 100 ma or so when drive is removed. Static current values much lower than this are preferred. In this way, the tubes are protected and there is no necessity for cutting off the plate voltage during receive periods. If the tripler acts unusual, a spurious oscillation around 1500 kHz may be present. This is due to the seven power-lead filters built into the unit. Its presence can be detected by placing a standard broadcast set near the rig and tuning around for the oscillation. The oscillation should be checked both during transmit and standby periods. It may be eliminated by connecting an 8-mfd capacitor directly from terminal C-119 to ground.

Modulation of this unit is indeed unique, as no modulator is required other than that in the Communicator. The system has been successfully employed for several years by the author in a 2C39 tripler for 1296-MHz service. Since output is primarily dependent on the drive power, the output will faithfully follow the modulation envelope of the Communicator. This is not a compromise system, as good quality modulation is produced. Actual modulation percentage is much higher than can be obtained with conventional plate modulation of this unit. The modulation fidelity is aided by the audio inverse feedback provided by the unbypassed R1.

A slight increase in output power can be obtained by experimenting with the output coupling link. The silver-plated steel unit is stiff and difficult to bend. Further, it is tied down by a ceramic standoff insulator. The link may be replaced by a piece of No. 12 copper wire and the standoff insulator removed and discarded. Series tuning of the link may help, but the total length of wire in the link must be quite short before resonance can be achieved. The output figure quoted above was achieved without series tuning.

For the boys who crave high power, a companion unit is available. This unit is identical to the tripler, except the input tunes to 432 MHz. The same power supply as used with the tripler can also supply the final. The 2C39s can give 50 watts output, and this output level could no doubt be reached with the drive power available from the tripler. The final

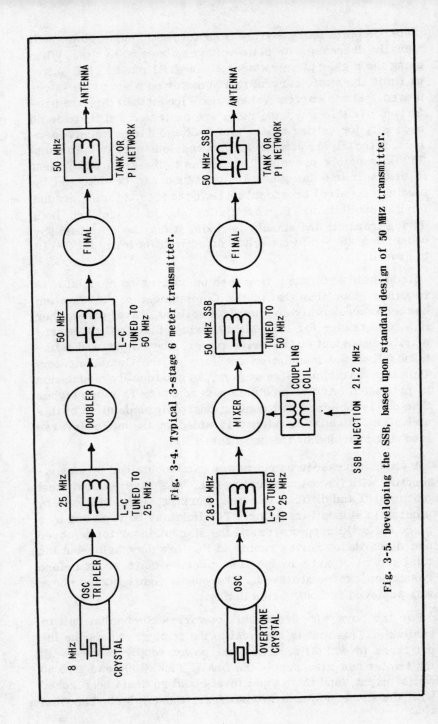

Fig. 3-4. Typical 3-stage 6 meter transmitter.

Fig. 3-5. Developing the SSB, based upon standard design of 50 MHz transmitter.

would require an external plate modulator, but who needs a modulator for straight CW?

Six-Meter Heterodyne Unit

There is a method for putting a SSB exciter on 6 meters without digging into the bank or present rig (much), and it is one of the first construction projects without any construction. After the unit was "debugged" it performed admirably.

Fig. 3-4 represents a typical 3-stage low-power 6 meter transmitter. If the coil-capacitor between the oscillator and the doubler is capable of resonating at 28 instead of 25 MHz, the change in Fig. 3-5 may be made. It is advisable to use a grid dip meter in making these adjustments. Fig. 3-6 is a schematic of the unit.

Here is an explanation of parts added:

28.805-MHz overtone crystal: The 28.805-MHz crystal was chosen because it is used in Citizen Band rigs as a receiving crystal and is therefore less expensive. An overtone crystal MUST be used or else unwanted harmonics will be produced and several unwanted byproducts will appear in the output. Any other mixing scheme may be used with appropriate coil changes.

Resistor in final cathode: A resistor was placed in the final cathode circuit to provide protective bias to prevent the final from burning up in the absence of drive. In a transmitter having a clamp tube or other device, this is unnecessary. The value of this resistor was chosen by experimentation, and when using a different final its value will change.

When the AM itch returns, all that need be done is turn the SSB exciter off, plug an 8-MHz crystal in, and after some retuning it's back on "ancient" modulation.

A Conservative 6-Meter Kilowatt

If you live in New England, maybe you'll want to be one of the chosen few to trade RST's with W4RMU on Sunday mornings. Or maybe when everyone else is working 300 miles on groundwave, you would like to work 400. To do these or any number of other worthwhile things on VHF, you need to overcome path attenuation. You need to scrounge around until you have enough db's to do the job.

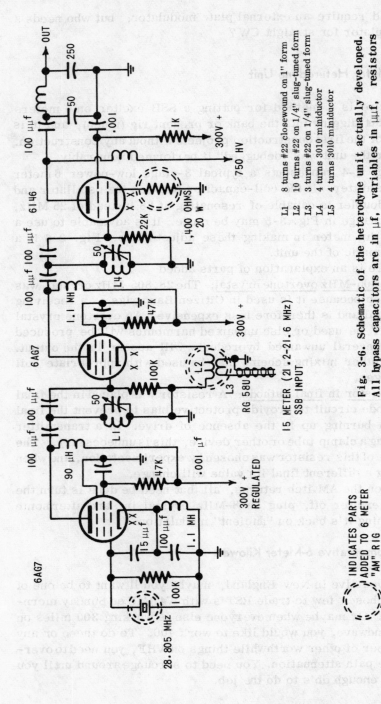

Fig. 3-6. Schematic of the heterodyne unit actually developed. All bypass capacitors are in μf, variables in μμf, resistors in ohms.

L1 8 turns #22 closewound on 1" form
L2 10 turns #22 on 1/4" slug-tuned form
L3 3 turns #22 on 1/4" slug-tuned form
L4 4 turns 3010 miniductor
L5 4 turns 3010 miniductor

So you look around. The antenna is still up, and maybe it will last through another season, but stacking is out of the question and so are a lot of other antenna schemes. So you look at the transmitter—it may be a 6146 or an 829B. Well, there's part of your answer. A kilowatt would represent about a twenty-time increase in power over the old 6146. Witness the following:

$$10 \log 20 = 13.0 \text{ db}$$

If you decide that two "S" units stand between you and your goal, the amplifier in Fig. 3-7 is practically a painless way of achieving the extra db. Designed to run a cool KW, this final is about as easy as they come, and it is well behaved.

The unit is constructed on a 17" x 10" x 3" chassis and a 10 1/2" rack panel. The tube sockets are mounted corner to corner on 5/8" spacers above the chassis so the grid terminals are about 3 1/2" apart. All pins, except the grids, are bypassed with .001-μf ceramics with as short leads as possible. Grid leaks are National poly feedthroughs that are soldered to the grid tuning capacitor terminals.

The plate circuit is somewhat breadboard, but properly shielded your TV won't know the difference. The plate capacitor is a dual-section 50 $\mu\mu$f with half of the plates removed and the remaining plates double spaced. To get the capacitor nearer the plate coil, it is mounted on aluminum brackets. The plate coil itself is mounted on two National 4" ceramic standoffs. The entire amplifier is shielded with sheet aluminum.

As mentioned before, this amplifier is well behaved, but it might require minor adjustments for maximum efficiency. With filament and bias voltages applied, adjust grid current drive to about 35 ma. If drive is marginal, C1 may be replaced by a 0-50 trimmer and peaked for maximum.

Next, apply screen and plate voltages. With no drive, there should be no grid, screen, or plate current. With the drive applied and the plate resonated, the screen current should be about 50 ma. When the amplifier runs unbalanced, spreading or squeezing the turns on one side of the grid coil should correct it. In operation no neutralization was necessary, but if instability exists, screen neutralization is recommended. If it is desired to operate this amplifier on AM phone type operation, it would be necessary to install a DC filter choke in series with the screen grid.

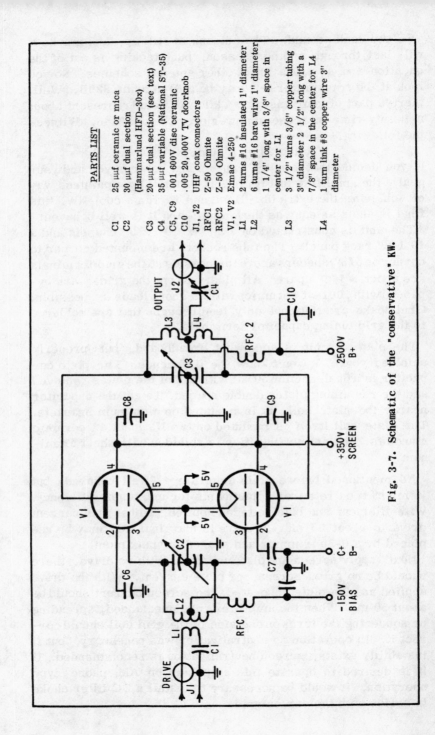

PARTS LIST

C1   25 μμf ceramic or mica
C2   30 μμf dual section
        (Hammarlund HFD-30x)
C3   20 μμf dual section (see text)
C4   35 μμf variable (National ST-35)
C5, C9 .001 600V disc ceramic
C10   .005 20,000V TV doorknob
J1, J2 UHF coax connectors
RFC1   Z-50 Ohmite
RFC2   Z-50 Ohmite
V1, V2 Eimac 4-250
L1   2 turns #16 insulated 1" diameter
L2   6 turns #16 bare wire 1" diameter
        1 1/4" long with 3/8" space in
        center for L1
L3   3 1/2" turns 3/8" copper tubing
        3" diameter 2 1/2" long with a
        7/8" space in the center for L4
L4   1 turn link #8 copper wire 3"
        diameter

Fig. 3-7. Schematic of the "conservative" KW.

48

A One-Transistor 6-Meter Rig

I have found this transistorized transmitter to operate on more of a novelty basis, but its value in basic theory cannot be overlooked. No modulator has yet been designed, but I am considering a Hiesing circuit now. The transmitter demonstrates the use of semiconductors at VHF frequencies, something which is too often overlooked. (See Fig. 3-8.)

Construction should be straightforward, and care should be taken to use the correct battery polarity. As you can see, the power supply is keyed, since no warm up time is required. Care should be taken to use only batteries and not battery eliminators, because any ripple present will show up on the signal.

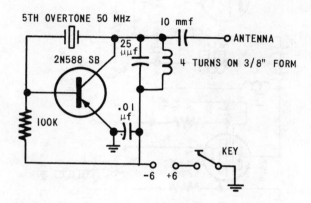

Fig. 3-8. The world's simplest 6-meter rig.

DX? Not quite, but one-mile operation has been accomplished using a receiver with 1 mv sensitivity.

500-Watt 6-Meter SSB Rig

Single sideband has been termed a miracle for the VHF pioneer. This in many ways is true, but in order to take utmost advantage, high power levels must be used. Since most available heterodyne units produce low power outputs, an additional unit, an amplifier, is required. The following is a description of a single unit that transforms a low-frequency signal to a high-power 6 meter job. See Fig. 3-9. A second desirable feature of this unit lies in its small size, allowing easy station

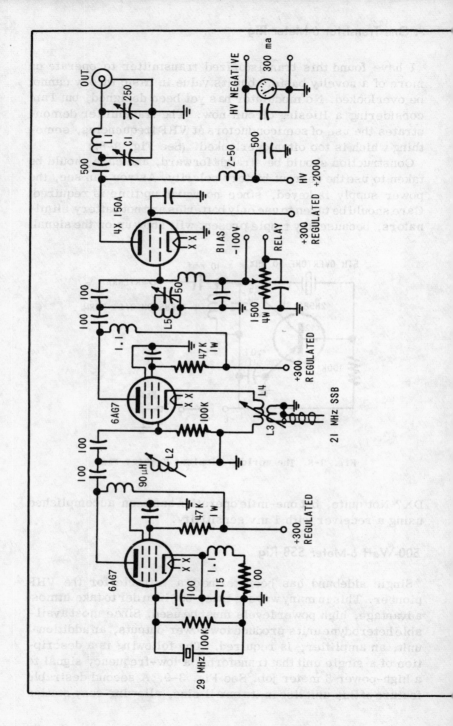

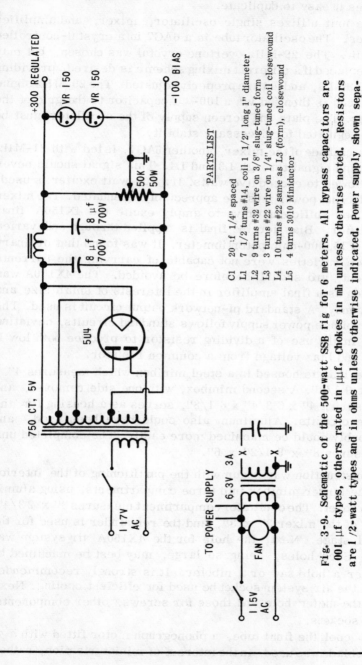

PARTS LIST

C1 20 µf 1/4" spaced
L1 7 1/2 turns #14, coil 1 1/2" long 1" diameter
L2 9 turns #32 wire on 3/8" slug-tuned form
L3 3 turns #22 wire on 1/4" slug-tuned form
L4 10 turns #22 same as L3 (form), closewound
L5 4 turns 3010 Miniinductor

Fig. 3-9. Schematic of the 500-watt SSB rig for 6 meters. All bypass capacitors are .001 µf types, others rated in µµf. Chokes in mh unless otherwise noted. Resistors are 1/2-watt types and in ohms unless otherwise indicated. Power supply shown separately, for those with their own available supplies.

51

assembly and transportation. The simplicity of the circuits makes it easy to duplicate.

The unit utilizes single oscillator, mixer, and amplifier stages. The oscillator tube is a 6AG7 in a crystal-controlled circuit. The 29-MHz overtone crystal was chosen, but may be replaced if a different mixing scheme is desired, providing that L2, L3, and L4 are properly adjusted. The 29-MHz signal produced is then fed via a 100-μμf capacitor to the grid of the mixer. The plate and screen supply of the oscillator must be well regulated for necessary stability.

The cathode of the mixer, another 6AG7, is fed with 21-MHz sideband signal through L3 and L4. This signal should never be allowed to exceed five watts. If a 100-watt exciter is used, the driving power must be appreciably attenuated. The mixer develops sufficient drive to amply excite the 4X150A final amplifier. Bias for the final is supplied through and varied with a 15,000-ohm potentiometer. It was found that ordinary carbon varieties were not capable of carrying the currents present, and should therefore be avoided. The 4X150A was chosen as a final amplifier in the interests of small size and efficiency. A standard pi-network output circuit is used. The low-voltage power supply follows standard circuits, deviating only in the use of a dividing resistor to produce both low B plus and bias voltage from a common resistor.

The unit is housed in a steel minibox which measures 4" x 6" x 9 1/2". A second minibox, with one side removed, and measuring 4" x 6 3/4" x 6 1/8", serves as a housing for the plate circuits. Aluminum also could have been used, and probably could be machined more easily. The completed unit measures 8" x 9 1/2" x 6".

Construction was begun with the partitioning of the interior of the larger minibox into three compartments, using aluminum sheet. The oscillator compartment measures 3" x 2 3/4", that of the mixer 3" x 3", and the remainder is used for the final stage. Next, the hole for the 4X150A air system was cut. Such holes, being so large, may best be machined by either a hole saw or a nibbler. It is strongly recommended that the air system socket be used for efficient cooling. Next, cut the meter hole and those for screws, other components, and sockets.

To cool the final tube, a phonograph motor fitted with a 4-inch blade was used, in the interest of miniaturization, rather than a large blower. Individual fan blades were twisted to reverse the flow of air. When fitted in place, this fan draws air through an opening in the bottom plate and forces it to escape through the air system socket, cooling the tube within. To increase the operating efficiency of this system, all holes or spaces remaining in the bottom cavity, after the completion of parts mounting, should be stopped up. The opening for the blade in the bottom plate should be only slightly larger than the blade itself, and perfectly centered. It will be found that it is easier to first wire the oscillator and mixer sockets and subassemblies, and then insert them into their respective cavities. Final connections may then be made, rather than attempt to complete the entire wiring in such a cramped space. When wiring the 4X150A socket, be sure to make all ground and bypass connections extremely short.

Contact to the anode cooler of the 4X150A is accomplished by means of a strip of 3/8" wide copper, bent into a circle and fastened together with a screw. Tightening this screw causes the copper band to grip the anode more firmly. The plate blocking and bypass capacitors are of the TV doorknob variety. Several vent holes should be drilled into the plate compartment to allow adequate escape of the forced air.

Upon completing the construction and carefully checking the wiring, it is recommended that a grid dip meter be used to approximate the coil settings and make any adjustments that prove necessary. Begin by applying filament voltage. The fan should begin to force air through the tube's anode cooler and out the top. After a few minutes, the 6AG7s should begin to feel warm. Now B-plus voltage and bias may be applied. It is highly advisable to start with about 600 volts on the plate of the final. Adjust the bias so that the static plate current is about 50 ma. This setting must be readjusted at a higher plate voltage. Provision has been made for the antenna relay to apply full bias during receive periods to cut off the tube.

After completing the above tests, apply drive and peak the oscillator and mixer controls for maximum output. Then dip the plate tuning control and load to the desired power level. If all goes well, apply the full 2,000 volts to the plate and readjust.

TVI, almost synonomous with 500 watts, is minimized with proper shielding and the use of a low-pass filter. In a few

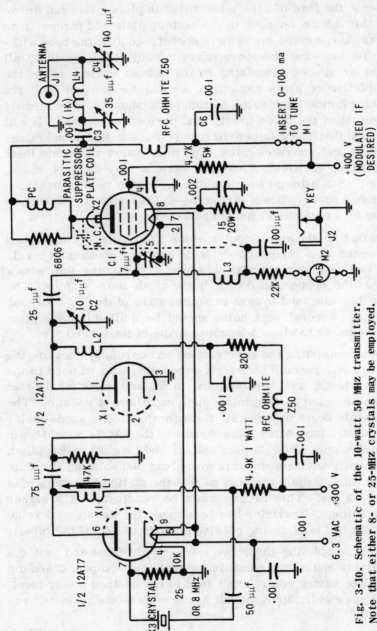

Fig. 3-10. Schematic of the 10-watt 50 MHz transmitter. Note that either 8- or 25-MHz crystals may be employed.

cases this may not be sufficient, since some have TVI difficulties at the 50-watt level even with the above precautions.

10-Watt 6-Meter Transmitter

Although 50-MHz transmitter designs can be found in almost any ham publication, the purpose of this job was to present a design utilizing parts and tubes which are common and easily obtained. This, we hope, will encourage more amateurs to get on the air.

The transmitter circuit diagram in Fig. 3-10 uses half of a 12AT7 as a frequency tripler and the other half as a doubler to obtain a 50-MHz signal from an 8-MHz crystal. If a 25-MHz crystal is used, only doubling action is required, and TVI possibilities are materially reduced. A TV horizontal deflection beam power tube, a 6BQ6, is used as a final. Input

L1	23 turns #30 enameled on 3/8" slug-tuned form
L2	Air-Dux #516t 3/8" long 5/8" diameter (use 6 turns)
L3	Air-Dux #516t (use 6 1/2" turns)
L4	Air-Dux #608t - 4 turns #18 3/4"
PC	2 1/2 turns #18 spaced 1 1/2 times wire diameter on 10 ohms 1/2 watt resistor
NC	See note in test
C1	Erie ceramic trimmer 1.5 - 7 μμf

Parts list for Fig. 3-10.

power to the final circuit, depending on the final plate voltage, is between 10 to 15 watts. The estimated output is 7 to 10 watts. The plate power supply requirements are 100 ma @ 300-500v for the 6BQ6 and 60 ma @ 300v for the 12AT7. A filament supply of 2 amps @ 6.3v is required for supplying both tubes. A closed-circuit jack, J-2, is provided for CW operation.

The transmitter is assembled in a 6" x 6" x 6" shielded box mounted on a 3" x 6" x 9" chassis. The assembly and positioning of components is shown in Fig. 3-11. The shielded box portion contains the final (6BQ6), parasitic suppressor (P.C.), output pi-network components (C3, C4, and L4), neutralization arrangement (nc). M1 (0 - 100 milliameter), and J1 the antenna output jack. M1 is used primarily for tuning up the transmitter and may be eliminated as a permanent feature. M2 (0 - 5 ma), C2, L1, X3 are mounted on the side of the chassis as shown.

Neutralization of the 6BQ6 is required. This is accomplished through nc (see schematic) which consists of a length of #16 rubber-covered solid wire attached to the lower portion of L3. This is brough through a 1/8" hole about 2 1/2" into the shielded box and cut to length for proper neutralization.

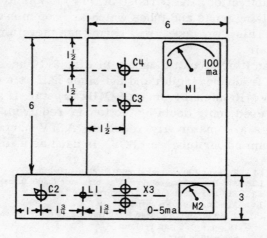

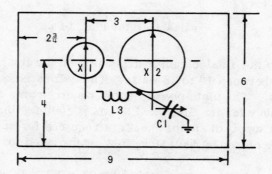

Fig. 3-11. Key dimensions for building the 10 watt 6 meter transmitter as a club project.

C6 is a .001-mfd feed-through capacitor. Mount L3 and C1 as close to pin 5 as possible. When tuning, C1 and C2 are used for adjusting the grid current of the 6BQ6 for a maximum reading. This reading of approximately 2 ma is obtained on M2. M1 is used along with C3 and C4 for tuning the plate circuit of the 6BQ6 to resonance. This will be indicated by a minimum plate current reading.

When wiring up the transmitter, make connections as short as possible. A review of VHF wiring procedure may be advisable before attempting construction. TVI suppression is incorporated in the circuit through the use of the pi-output network, parasitic suppressor pc, and neutralization. However, proper bypassing and shielding are necessary for additional reduction.

Modulators

A few possible modulators and mike inputs which may be used with this transmitter are:

1. Crystal mike input
   "Low Power Modulator"
   ARRL Handbook, 1960, page 271
   Tubes used (1) 12AX7, (1) 6C4, (2) 6AQ5
   Power supply 90 ma @ 500v DC

2. Single button carbon mike input
   "Simple Modulator for Portable Work"
   ARRL Hints & Kinks, Vol. #3, page 48
   Tubes used (2) 6V6GT
   Power supply 75-100 ma @ 200-300v DC

Two-Meter 829B Final Amplifier

I have built different final amplifiers in the last year or so, using the 829B, with hairpin loops and 1/4 and 1/2 wavelength lines for the tuned circuits. Using a plate tank, composed of a coil and capacitor, results were very poor; not much RF output but lots of heat. Next, half wave capacity-loaded lines, folded back on themselves to conserve space, were tried. These were a great improvement, but you can't crowd tuned lines into a small chassis and keep the lines balanced. It was then decided to build the final amplifier on a more roomy chassis, so the lines could be all by themselves. The junk box provided about all of the necessary parts. The chassis that the unit is built on had been used for other projects and had holes like a sieve.

The plate lines are made from 5/16" diameter copper tubing, spaced 7/8" between centers (Fig. 3-12). The plate caps for the 829B were my biggest problem. Every time I thought of buying commercial heat-dissipating caps, I could hear cash registers ringing up a lot of money. Again the junk box was consulted. I found some old metal binding posts that were very popular in the early days of radio. These were used on battery radios to provide the connections to the wires going to

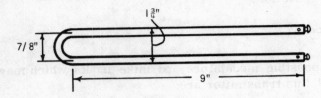

Fig. 3-12. Plate lines, top view. Lines are 3/8" diameter copper tubing.

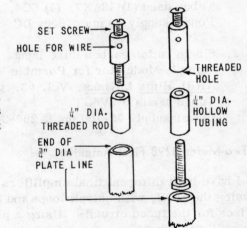

Fig. 3-13. Two different types of binding posts which are used to connect plate lines to the 829B.

the batteries. Two types of these are shown in Fig. 3-13. I believe these are sill quite popular in the junk boxes of many ham shacks. The first type is screwed into a 1/4" diameter piece of threaded rod. I found in my junk box a couple of metal threaded spacers which worked out nicely. The second type, a 1/4" diameter, hollow metal spacer is connected to the binding post. The copper tubing used has an inside diameter just large enough so that the metal spacer, connected to the metal binding post, can be driven tightly into the end of the copper rod. I heated the end of the copper rod and put solder down into it to make a real solid connection between the binding post and the copper rod.

The lines are spaced a distance between centers equal to the distance between the two plate pins on the 829B. At the other end of the lines, the tubing is bent at a right angle, flattened, drilled, bolted together, then soldered. When the lines are finished, they look like a tuning fork, and if the two holes are positioned just right they will slip right over the plate pins on the 829B. These holes have to be in the right position because, when the screws in the binding post are tightened, you can crack the seal very easily on the 829B. These lines also conduct heat from the plate of the 829B very nicely. Of course, the tuned lines could be made of solid rods by drilling and threading the ends to fit a screw. Two holes would have to be drilled for the plate pins to fit through. The tuning capacitor is connected 1 3/4" from the shorted end of the lines. By connecting it way down on the line, instead of up close to the tube, longer lines can be used, and secondly, it makes the plate tuning much less touchy when it comes to dipping the final. The butterfly capacitor used was the final tuning capacitor from a defunct 522 transmitter. This was marked Part #117 in schematics and is rated 2.8 to 11.0 $\mu\mu$f. It has three rotor and three stator plates per section. I believe some surplus companies are selling units similar to this at a reasonable price. A larger value could be used by connecting it nearer the shorted section. The lines are for the most part supported at the shorted end by a short flexible piece of metal. See Fig. 3-14.

The butterfly capacitor was mounted below the lines on a support made of insulating material. Two short wires, about one inch long, go from the stator sections at the back of the capacitor up to the lines where they are soldered on. These two wires add a bit more support for the lines. The rest of the support comes from the 829B itself. The tuning capacitor is turned with a shaft made of a polystyrene rod the same diameter as the tuning capacitor shaft. With a butterfly capacitor, from minimum to maximum capacity is only 1/4 of a turn of the shaft, so a 3-to-1 vernier drive was used on this capacitor. Those cute little Japanese vernier dials on the market would really fill the bill here. The shaft of the butterfly can

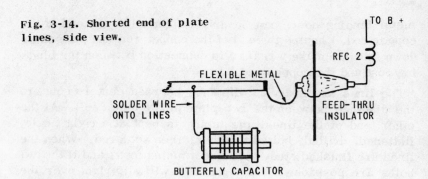

Fig. 3-14. Shorted end of plate lines, side view.

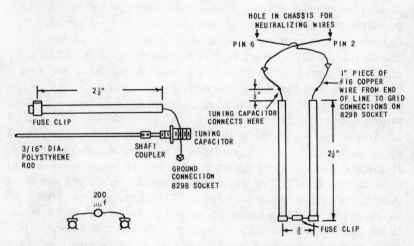

Fig. 3-15. Grid lines, top view. Lines are 1/4" diameter copper tubing. Grid lines, end view, showing fuse clips with 200 μμf capacitor soldered between. Grid lines, side view.

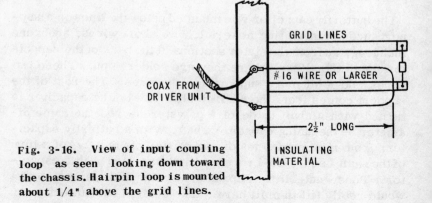

Fig. 3-16. View of input coupling loop as seen looking down toward the chassis. Hairpin loop is mounted about 1/4" above the grid lines.

be coupled to the plastic rod by fitting a piece of spaghetti tubing over the shafts where they couple together and adding a drop of cement. As the shaft of the butterfly turns easily, this method works well with no slippage. At the other end, to get the 3/16" rod to fit into a 1/4" knob, either wrap plastic tape around the rod to increase its diameter or drive the rod into a 1/4" diameter metal shaft with a hold-through metal shaft coupler; this is necessary because the rotor section should not be grounded.

The grid lines are made with 1/4" diameter copper tubing, spaced 3/4" between centers. See Fig. 3-15. A moveable short was made by taking two fuse clips and soldering between them a 200-$\mu\mu$f small mica or ceramic capacitor. This capacitor was used between the two clips, instead of a shorting bar made of metal, for two reasons: First, using the capacitor made the lines physically longer. Due to the high input capacity of the 829A a 1/4-wavelength line is very short, so this method was used to lengthen them. Secondly, the amount of grid current for both sections of the tube can be measured separately at the junction of R1-R3 and R2-R4 by measuring the negative voltage at these points. This way it shows if one half of the tube is receiving more drive than the other half. With a shorting bar you can't check to see if the input to the tube is balanced or not. The tuning capacitor is a midget butterfly job mounted between the tuned lines by the two connections from its stators. This is the only support required for this capacitor, since it is very small and light. A plastic rod was used with this shaft also, as the rotor section should not be grounded. A J38 mike jack was used for a bushing where the rod comes through the front of the chassis. This 3/16" rod is about the size of the inner shaft of concentric TV volume controls, so by filing one side of the rod flat, TV knobs will fit nicely. With a grid dipper, tune the lines to the 2 meter band with the movable shorting capacitor. Later tuning is all done with the midget variable. The hairpin loop used to couple from the exciter into the lines is a single turn of the wire, 2 1/2" long by 3/4" wide, mounted about 1/4" above the grid lines, positioned as shown in Fig. 3-16.

The tube is neutralized by crossing two wires from the grids of the tube and passing them up through small holes drilled in the chassis. These wires extend about 1 inch above the chassis along the sides of the tube and are made of a stiff in-

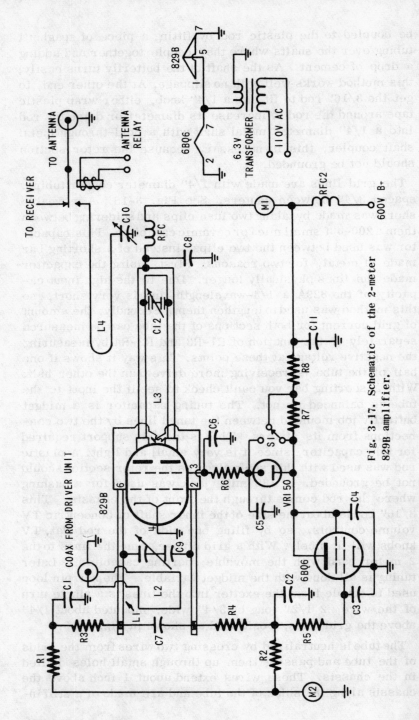

Fig. 3-17. Schematic of the 2-meter 829B amplifier.

sulated wire (#18 or so). The tube was neutralized the regular way—by applying grid drive and running the plate tuning capacitor through resonance and adjusting the neutralizing wires so that the grid drive doesn't vary. Neutralization can be checked when the rig is completed by first applying drive to the final (with no plate voltage) and adjusting the input capacitor to resonance. Next, apply high voltage (with no load) and dip the final. Maximum grid drive should occur at the same spot that the final dips. With plate current at minimum (plate dip), by tuning the plate capacitor either direction off resonance the grid drive should drop as the plate current rises. This 829B did not neutralize exactly like the method outlined, but was very close. See Fig. 3-17 for the complete schematic.

The 829B socket was mounted on the top of the chassis above

S1	SPDT switch	C3, C4	.001 mfd 600V ceramic
M1	250 ma meter	C5, C6	500 μμf disc ceramic 600V
M2	20 ma meter	C7	200 μμf mica or ceramic
RFC1	Ohmite Z-144	C8	500 μμf 2500V transmitting
RFC2	Ohmite Z-144		mica
R1, R2	10K, 2 watt	C9	1.8 - 8.7 μμf miniature
R3, R4	1K, 1/2 watt		butterfly E. F. Johnson type
R5	1K, 1/2 watt		5MB11
R6	100 ohm, 1 watt carbon	C10	10 μμf variable
R7	3K, 5 watt wire-wound	C11	.001 mfd 2500V mica
R8	15K, 20 watt wire-wound	C12	2.8 to 11.0 μμf butterfly
C1, C2	.001 mfd 600V ceramic		see text

Parts list for Fig. 3-17.

a 2 1/2" diameter hole. This makes for a short cathode ground lead, which is desirable. The socket was mounted so that the cathode lead (the big pin) was toward the front of the chassis. The final is driven from an exciter which uses a 2E26 as a doubler from 72 MHz as its final. With this low power driver, 12 to 14 ma of grid drive can be obtained at a plate power input of 125 watts to the 829B.

A one-turn hairpin loop is used to couple from the plate line, and C10 is used as a loading capacitor. The capacitor used for this purpose should have a very low minimum capacity. The antenna changeover relay was built right into the rig at the end of the pick-up loop.

A screen grid clamp tube is used so that the rig can be used on CW, and it also serves as protection for the final should drive fail. For use on CW the switch on the final amplifier is put into CW position, which cuts out the 3000-ohm screen grid resistor and at the same time places the VR150 in series with the screen lead. The driver unit is keyed when used on CW. With the key up, the plate current on the 829B is about 15 ma. If the rig is keyed when the phone/CW switch is in phone position, the plate current, with the key up, would be around 75 ma which would soon overheat the tube. A single-turn loop of wire was soldered to the base of a 60-watt bulb and held close to the plate lines. With about 110 watts input to the final, full brilliance was obtained from the bulb.

CHAPTER 4

VHF Antennas

VHF work calls for changes in antenna design techniques. At such frequencies the physical size is reduced to the point where an antenna having some gain over a simple dipole can be used in almost any location. Therefore, experimentation with various arrays is an important phase in the program of progressive VHF'ers.

Cubical Quad for 6 Meters and Up

Cubical Quad antennas for the VHF bands above 144 MHz are very easy to construct and adjust for maximum forward gain and front-to-back ratio. Front-to-back ratios of 45 db and front-to-side ratios of well over 60 db are obtained with proper adjustments of the quad. An excellent job of tuning up the quad is done simply by using a single loop with the same dimensions as the driven element minus the tuning stub, with a crystal diode connected to the feed point. The output of the diode is filtered and fed to a meter through a long shielded cable. This is necessary as this loop must be placed at least 6 wavelengths from the antenna being adjusted and the meter at the antenna in order to make the tuning adjustments of the shorting stubs. All adjustments can be done at ground level with excellent results. As with all antennas, best results are usually obtained with the antenna in its operating position, as this places the antenna a good portion or better of a wavelength above ground. It's very easy to place the antenna one wavelength above ground for 2 meters and up by the use of a tall stepladder, with the top surface area of the ladder below the bottom elements of the quad. The detector loop must be at the same height as the antenna and in the same plane. The meter used should have several current ranges between 50 microamps and ten ma.

The quad can be made very simply and inexpensively by the use of #10 copper wire (or larger) and some 1 x 2 furring strips. See Fig. 4-1. Aluminum wire also could be used, but it is difficult to solder to. It is advisable to use wood screws

I X 2 FURRING STRIP

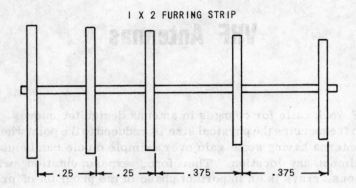

Fig. 4-1. Side view of quad frame, showing separation dimension.

Fig. 4-2. Construction of an insulator block. See text.

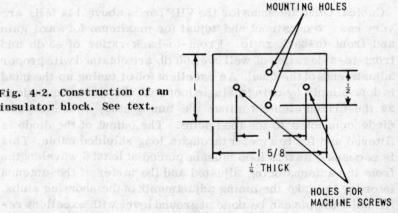

when fastening the vertical support arms to the boom and to give the wood a good painting. Vertical supports, made by splitting the 1" x 2" piece in half, are cut long enough to support the loop. Aluminum tubing could be used for the boom and vertical supports, if the loops are supported by good high frequency insulators.

Small blocks (Fig. 4-2) of polystyrene, phenol fiber, or such are used to support the split side of the loops. Small pieces of rod or flat stock can be used for support of the opposite side. Polyrod is nice, as the wire can be heated and pressed into it. The simplest way to fasten this side is to use a small flathead wood screw and solder the wire to it after the screw is in place. The quad in use at present is a 5-element job using this type of construction (brass screw), fed with 35 feet of RG 59/AU coax, with 12 watts input to a 832A. I have managed to work 7 states in less than 6 months on 220 MHz.

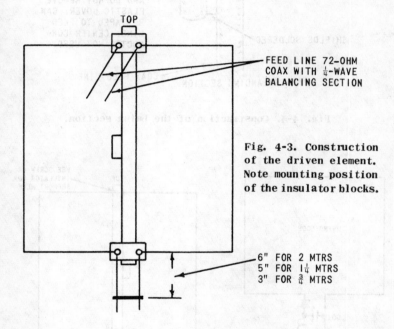

TOP

FEED LINE 72-OHM
COAX WITH ¼-WAVE
BALANCING SECTION

Fig. 4-3. Construction
of the driven element.
Note mounting position
of the insulator blocks.

6" FOR 2 MTRS
5" FOR 1¼ MTRS
3" FOR ¾ MTRS

It is advisable to stick to an odd number of elements if more than 3 are to be used.

The full length of the driven loop (Fig. 4-3) is found by multiplying the free-space wavelength in inches by 1.05. Spacing between the reflector and driven elements is either .2 or .25 wavelengths and .25 for the first director. The spacing should increase to .375 for each additional director. The directors could be all of the same size or reduced 5% in size from the preceding one, as in the case of the Yagi antenna. See Table 4-I.

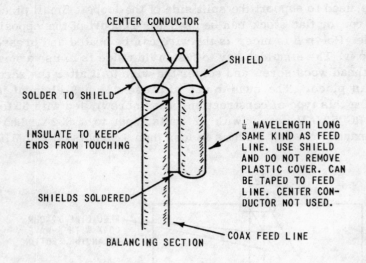

Fig. 4-4. Construction of the balun section.

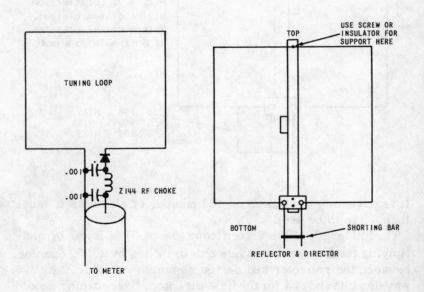

Fig. 4-5. Construction of tuning loop (at left), and the
reflector and director.

In the past, the driven element has been fed with 72-ohm coax with a quarterwave balancing section (Fig. 4-4). During warm weather, we feed the antenna through a gamma match and compare the two feed systems. The boys who used the quad for 2 and 1 1/4 feel that they would gain by going over to the gamma match, as this would give a better match as more elements are added.

To tune the antenna, it is connected to a low-power transmitter set for the desired portion of the band to be used and pointed forward, directly at the loop. See Fig. 4-5. The driven element is adjusted first for maximum reading on the meter, then the reflector and first director right down the line. There is quite a reaction between the elements so be sure you readjust each element in the same order, until no further increase can be obtained on the meter reading. You can check the front-to-back ratio by swinging the beam around 180° and noting the meter reading. The reading will be very low and could possibly be reduced more by touching up the tuning on the reflector. Do not move the shorting bar too much or you will have to turn the beam around again and recheck the tuning on the driven element. You will need the 50 microamp scale on your meter to check the reflector and the milliampere scale

Table 4-1. Method for determining antenna dimensions.

Wavelength (meters)	$=$	$\dfrac{300}{f\ (MHz)}$
Meters X 39.37" X .984	$=$	This answer is then multiplied by 1.05 and divided by 4 which will give the length of each side of the square of the driven loop.
Reflector	$=$	1.05 X driven element length
Director	$=$	.95 X driven element length
Length of side = 2 meters	$=$	Reflector (22.5") Driven element (21.5") Director (20.5")
1 1/4 meters	$=$	Reflector (13.5") Driven element (13.0") Director (12.5")

for the forward gain. When all adjustments have been completed, solder the shorting bar in place permanently.

A Compact 6-Meter Beam

The need for a compact 6 meter beam originally arose because our antenna had to be mounted in the attic. With a sloping roof only 5 feet high at the apex and with a number of vertical risers, there was nowhere near the space necessary to rotate a beam with half-wave elements. Because of the height limitation a quad employing quarter-wave elements also was out of the question. The 3-element beam that was finally designed and built has the gain (7 db) of a full size antenna, yet the turning radius is only 9 feet. Because the design lends itself

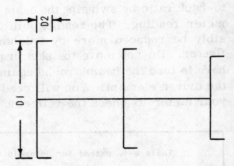

Fig. 4-6. Physical layout of the compact 6-meter beam, showing bends.

to a type of construction that would permit the rapid assembly and disassembly of the beam, it would seem practical to also employ it for portable operation. Since the longest element is only 58 inches, there should be little trouble in stowing the collapsed beam in the trunk of a car.

The small size of the beam is based on a well known principle: The intensity of the field radiated from a conductor is proportional to the current. Since in a half-wave element the current is greatest at the center and falls off rapidly toward the ends, maximum radiation occurs around the center of the element. The last 1/8 wavelength on each end of a half-wave dipole contributes very little to the field intensity. If you are thinking, at this point, that we could chop these ends off and have left a quarter-wave radiator with almost the same efficiency as a full-sized antenna, you are right. Unfortunately, problems of radiation and surge impedance arise which prevent matching such an antenna to ordinary transmission lines in a simple way. We can, however, take those 1/8 wavelength ends and bend them downwards, at right angles to the center 1/4 wavelength of the dipole. In this way, the lengths of the elements can be 1/2 wavelength long and still occupy only half the space of ordinary dipoles. The finished 3-element beam, based on this idea, appears to be an ordinary one, except that the elements each look like an inverted U, as shown in Fig. 4-6.

The lengths and spacings necessary to construct the beam are given in Table 4-II. The lengths of the overall elements are a few inches longer than are generally found in various

Table 4-II. Element length and spacing for a 6-meter beam.

ELEMENT	D1	D2	SPACING
Reflector	58"	29.5"	34" (.15 λ) to radiator
Radiator	56"	28"	
Director	54"	27"	46" (.20 λ) to radiator

Gamma — approx. 12" long spaced 2" from radiator tuned with a 50 μμfd variable condenser.

Elements and gamma rod match made from 1/4" diameter aluminum rod or tubing. For indoor operation aluminum ground wire is suitable.

handbooks. This is so because a correction is necessary due to the two bends in the elements. The beam was gamma matched to 75-ohm coax. The lengths in Table 4-II are for gamma match for this line impedance. However, 50-ohm cable will work as well simply by shortening the length of the gamma rod. Tuning a gamma matched beam of this type is no different than a full-sized beam. Just follow the directions in any of the several handbooks. When completed and placed in operation in the attic the beam was found to have an SWR of less than 1.5 from 50 to 51.5 MHz.

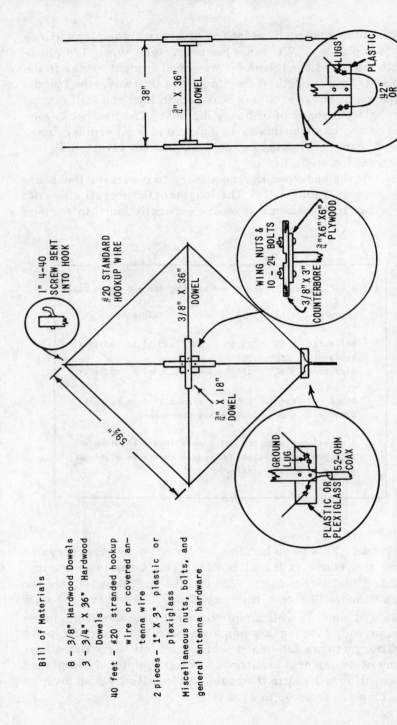

Bill of Materials

8 – 3/8" Hardwood Dowels

3 – 3/4" X 36" Hardwood Dowels

40 feet – #20 stranded hookup wire or covered antenna wire

2 pieces– 1" X 3" plastic or plexiglass

Miscellaneous nuts, bolts, and general antenna hardware

1" 4-40 SCREW BENT INTO HOOK

#20 STANDARD HOOKUP WIRE

3/8" X 36" DOWEL

3/4" X 18" DOWEL

59½"

WING NUTS & 10 - 24 BOLTS

3/4"X 6"X 6" PLYWOOD

3/8" X 3" COUNTERBORE

GROUND LUG

52-OHM COAX

PLASTIC OR PLEXIGLASS

LUGS

PLASTIC

42" OR 43" STUB

38"

3/4" X 36" DOWEL

Fig. 4-7. Layout of collapsible cubical quad.

A 6-Meter Cubical Quad

The schematic diagram in Fig. 4-7 shows a 6 meter collapsible portable cubical quad antenna. It was put into successful operation on two different weekends where some 57 stations were worked in one Sunday afternoon.

A Cylindrical Parabolic Antenna

A cylindrical parabolic antenna, as compared with a parabola of revolution, has the disadvantage of having less gain and the inability to change polarization readily. However, its gain is sufficient for moonbounce communications, and its construc-

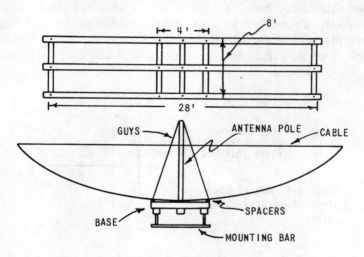

Fig. 4-8. Actual construction of the parabolic antenna.

tion is easier, faster, and less expensive. The cylindrical parabolic reflector shown in Fig. 4-8 was constructed of wood and chicken wire. The shape of the curve was derived from the formula: $Y^2 = 4px$.

In the formula $Y^2 = 4px$, (1/4X, 6Y) represents the coordinates of any point on a parabolic curve (Fig. 4-9). The value of X is the distance in front of the base of the parabola and the value of Y is the distance offset from the center. For example: If you decide to construct a parabolic reflector with a distance across the mouth of 28 feet and a depth of 4 feet, 4 feet would be the X distance and 14 feet would be the offset from the center of the point at the end of this parabola. (Center can be referred to as the Y distance). By substituting X and Y in the formula, the focal distance, p, can be derived.

$$Y^2 = 4\ px$$
$$(14)^2 = 4\ p\ (4)$$
$$106 = 16\ p$$
$$p = 12.25$$

Once the focal distance is determined, you can determine the Y distance for a given X distance and vice versa.

The first step in the parabola's physical construction was the assembly of the base. To the base was attached six lengths of redwood, 1" x 2" x 16'. Across the ends of the six lengths were placed two 8-foot pieces of redwood, 1" x 2". Chicken wire, four feet wide and one inch mesh, was then stapled be-

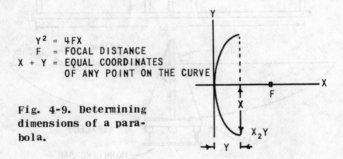

$Y^2 = 4FX$
F = FOCAL DISTANCE
$X + Y$ = EQUAL COORDINATES
OF ANY POINT ON THE CURVE

Fig. 4-9. Determining dimensions of a parabola.

tween the outside and center pieces. The next step was to place spacers between the edge of the base and six redwood pieces which make up the frame. Three cables were cut to a length of 27 feet, the distance across the opening of the parabola, and fastened between the ends of the frame. The parabola then had an approximate parabolic curve. The wood took the shape of a parabola because when pressure is applied to the end of a length of wood and is equally transmitted through the wood, the wood takes the shape of a parabola. This fact may be proven by taking measurements at different points on the curve. A pole was bolted to the center of the reflector and guyed to the base to support the primary antenna. A metal pole was bolted across the back of the base for the purpose of mounting; finally,

74

after the parabola is mounted, the ends of the frame should be guyed to a point on the back of the parabola for rigidity.

A Base-Loaded Whip for 6 Meters

The very popular Heath Sixer has been modified by many until only the name-plate remains to clearly identify it. The designers of this transceiver included one feature that seems to have been completely overlooked by most hams—the handle! When I built my Sixer I had one thought in mind—an ideal portable rig for traveling light. However, my traveling plans didn't include enough wire to string a dipole and a roll of coax to feed it. Even when it is possible to cart a case of cable around, most portable locations leave much to be desired when it comes to hanging the antenna.

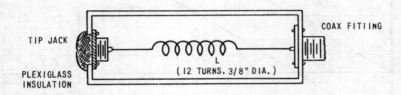

Fig. 4-10. Interior of the base loading coil housing, showing construction and coil data.

The answer was an antenna that was light and small enough to pack inconspicuously—specifically, a base-loaded whip that could be installed and removed conveniently. Here's the way it works: The base loading coil consists of 12 turns of uninsulated hook-up wire wound on a 3/8-inch form. The turns are spaced a wire's diameter apart. The whip measures 36 inches, and in my case was made from a straightened coat hanger soldered to a tip-jack plug. For other mechanical details see Fig. 4-10.

The mechanical modifications are limited only by the builder's imagination and specific needs. For my purpose, I constructed the loading coil unit in a piece of U-shaped aluminum with a coax fitting on one end and an insulated tip-jack at the other end. The coil was soldered between the two.

For the utmost portability, I assembled the finished unit in a small box taken from the surplus junk pile (miniboxes will

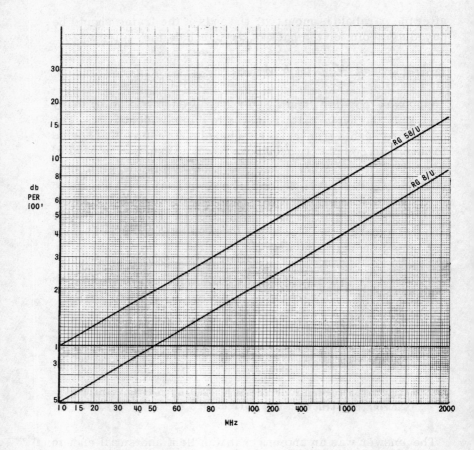

Fig. 4-11. Graph showing coax cable losses.

do here) and mounted it directly to the back of the Sixer case.
A short length of coax with plugs on both ends allows the connection of the loading unit in seconds. When another antenna
is to be used, it is only necessary to unplug the connecting
coax and couple the other line to the regular fitting. As with
any antenna, a good ground is important, and the loading coil
mounting box should be well grounded to the case.

Reports have ranged from as good, compared to the dipole
I had been using, to an increase of from 3 to 4 "S" units over
the dipole. This little antenna is no DX'er, but it sure does
a fine job with the locals, and finally justifies the handle on
top of the Sixer!

Coaxial Cables for VHF

The antenna feed line often is the weak link in the amateur station. It contributes nothing but losses; perhaps that is why its effect is so frequently overlooked. The general rule seems to be to use a piece of coax of the correct nominal impedance and forget it. On the lower bands this doesn't do much harm, but above 50 MHz, line losses can easily consume 75% of the transmitter output or the signal into the receiver. There is no one "best" cable for any particular installation. The amount of losses that can be tolerated must be weighed against the cost and availability of various cables. However, it is interesting to note that some of the most common coax types should not be used in any serious installation.

Table 4-III. Losses in 75-ohm coax cable.

RG/U	COST	DIAMETER	JACKET	100 MHz	1000 MHz
6, 6A	$15.00	.332	2	2.8	11.0
11	9.00	.405	1	2.1	7.8
11A	12.00	.405	2	2.1	7.8
12	19.00	.475	2A	2.1	7.8
13	17.00	.420	1	2.1	7.8
13A	18.00	.420	2	2.1	7.8
59	4.00	.242	1	3.8	14.0
59A, B	5.00	.242	2	9 @ 400	9 @ 400
140	–	HI – Temperature 59A/U			–
144	–	HI – Temperature 11/U			–
216	–	Same as 13A/U		–	–

The losses in the antenna feedline (Fig. 4-11, Tables 4-III and 4-IV) of course are equal on transmit and receive; usually it is the latter that requires most consideration, for the limits on receiver sensitivity inhibit VHF activity more than transmitter power.

Tables 4-III and 4-IV list most of the available coax types. Most are for reference, being seldom available to the amateur. The data is reduced to that of importance in hamming: impedance, diameter, jacket material, attenuation at 100 and 1000 MHz, and price. Prices are approximate, taken

77

Table 4-IV. Losses in 50-ohm coax cable.

RG/U	COST	DIAMETER	JACKET	100 MHz	1000 MHz
5	$11.00	.332	1	2.6	9.5
5B	24.00	.328	-	2.4	8.8
8	9.50	.405	1	2.1	9.0
8A	12.50	.405	2	2.1	9.0
9	23.00	.420	2	2.0	8.5
9A	30.00	.420	2	2.3	8.6
9B	30.00	.420	2	2.3	8.6
10	19.50	.475	2A	2.3	9.0
10A	20.50	.475	2	2.1	9.0
14	23.00	.545	2	1.4	6.2
14A	27.00	.545	2	1.4	6.2
17	48.00	.870	2	.85	4.2
17A	52.50	.870	2	.85	4.2
18	65.00	.948	2A	.85	4.2
18A	68.00	.945	2A	.85	4.2
19,19A	83.00	1.120	2	.68	3.5
54	-	.275	1	3.1	12
54A	7.50	.250	3	3.1	12
55	8.00	.206	3	4.2	16.0
58	4.00	.195	1	4.2	16.0
58A	-	.195	1	5.3	22.0
58B	-	.195	2	4.2	16.0
58C	5.00	.195	2	5.3	22.0
74,74A	40.00	.615	2A	1.4	6.2
141A	-	HI - Temperature RG58C/U			-
142A	-	HI - Temperature RG55A/U			-
147	-	Same as 19 w/armor			3.5
148	-	Same as 8 w/armor			-
159	-	HI - Temperature 55			-
212	-	Same as RG58/U			
213	-	Same as RG8A/U			
214	-	Same as RG9B/U			
215	-	Same as RG10A/U			
218	-	Same as RG17A/U			
223	-	Same as RG55A/U			
224	-	Same as RG74A/U			

78

from a bulk, net list, and generally are lower than the short-length over-the-counter cost.

It is important when buying coax to be sure you are getting cable meeting the military specifications for the particular type. There are many cables available, advertised as having characteristics similar to an RG/U type. These may or may not be worth using; the major manufacturers sell only cables inspected for conformity to specification in all regards. A very important characteristic usually overlooked is the jacket material. The vinyl jacket contains a plasticizer to obtain flexibility; many common plasticizers will migrate from the jacket into the inner dielectric. This is a continuing process from the day of manufacture. The effect is to alter the impedance and greatly increases losses. A type I jacket contains such a migrating plasticizer; cable with type I jacket material has a useful life possibly as short as one year and very seldom as much as three years. This, of course, is to say that the WW II surplus RG/8U (which is type I) is essentially worthless. Type II and other jacket materials contain noncontaminating plasticizers and should be useful for ten, fifteen years, or even longer. Obviously, then, if the antenna is to stay up a few years, type I coax should not be considered, even though it is a bit cheaper.

What coax should be chosen for a particular installation? Many cables on the list are special and not commonly available. For 50-ohm line it is best to choose among RG58B/U, RG58C/U, RG8A/U (or RG213/U), RG17/U, RG17A/U (or RG218/U), or Times T4/50. For 75-ohm line use RG59A/U, RG59B/U, RG11A/U, Times JT204, or Belden 8213. The common cables with type I jacket material are RG5/U, RG8/U, RG54/U, RG58 /U, RG58A/U, RG11/U, and RG59/U. The group (which includes virtually all transmission lines in use) is not recommended. The useful life is too short. The information in Table 4-III will aid in determining the loss of any coax at any frequency. Simply plot the two attenuation figures given in Table 4-III and draw a straight line through these two points. RG58 B/U and RG8A/U are already plotted.

CHAPTER 5

Power Supply Considerations

As plans for a new rig developed, it became apparent that four power supplies would be required: A supply for a 417A converter, a 750v-300ma final supply, a 300v supply for RF and modulator stages, and a bias supply. With this much construction contemplated, it seemed wise to do a little studying of power supply principles and considerable planning before starting.

The converter supply was suggested by Carl Scheilder, W2AZL. This idea, shown in Fig. 5-1, makes an excellent converter supply. Two small 6v filament transformers connected back-to-back supply plenty of B plus at around 110v, depending on the bleeder resistor used, plus 6v for filaments.

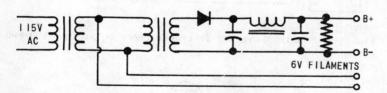

Fig. 5-1. Converter power supply, suggested by W2AZL.

This same idea can be put to work in an existing supply if enough room is available. Connect a small filament transformer as shown to the filament leads of a multivoltage transformer and get the same results.

There is considerable activity in this area on the VHF bands. A 100-watt signal is not needed for local work. Besides, several of the fellows are near enough to be really bothered by that much power. For these reasons, it was decided that a good means of reducing power was a primary consideration. A Variac is the first choice; however, I had none and they aren't cheap. TV transformers are available at a buck or so each and deliver up to 400v each side of center tap. Perhaps a matched pair could be used to accomplish the voltage dropping.

Fig. 5-2 shows two TV transformers with primaries connected in parallel and secondaries in series to produce 700v to 800v DC for the final. A switch or relay can be used to make use of one or both of the transformers for final voltage. This idea was discarded because at one-half voltage or, in other words, using single-transformer half-wave rectification might prove difficult with the oil-filled electrolytics I was planning to use for filters.

Fig. 5-3 shows a similar setup with an additional rectifier

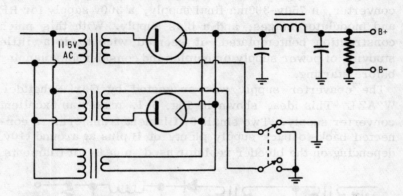

Fig. 5-2. Supply using two TV transformers to produce 700-800 volts.

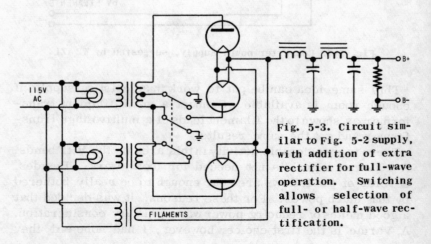

Fig. 5-3. Circuit similar to Fig. 5-2 supply, with addition of extra rectifier for full-wave operation. Switching allows selection of full- or half-wave rectification.

82

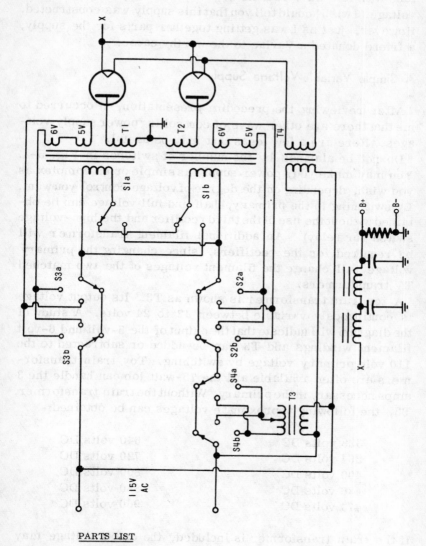

Fig. 5-4. Schematic of simple variable-voltage power supply.

tube with full-wave rectification. Switching gives full or half
voltage. I wish I could tell you that this supply was constructed.
However, just as I was getting together parts for the supply,
a friend donated a Variac to the worthy cause.

A Simple Variable-Voltage Supply

After reviewing the preceding presentation, it occurred to
me that there are other ways of controlling power supply voltages. Here are a few ideas that may be useful.

Do not be alarmed by the number of switches in Fig. 5-4.
You may make your power supply as simple or as complex as
you wish, depending on the degree of voltage control you want.
By switching in the primary, half and full voltage can be obtained without the use of the third rectifier and the high-voltage
switch (or relay). An additional filament transformer will
be required for the rectifiers, since changing the primary
voltage will change the filament voltages of the two matched
TV transformers.

A toy train transformer is shown as T3. Its output voltage
is continuously variable between 12 to 24 volts. A study of
the diagram will indicate that the output of the 5-volt and 6-volt
filament windings and T3 can be added or subtracted to the
110 volt primary voltage by switching. Toy train transformers are often available and the 75-watt job can handle the 3
amps necessary in the primary. Without the train transformer,
T3, the following approximate voltages can be obtained:

328 volts DC	640 volts DC
264 volts DC	720 volts DC
400 volts DC	800 volts DC
436 volts DC	880 volts DC
473 volts DC	960 volts DC

If the train transformer is included, the output voltage may
be varied from 290 volts to over 1000 volts DC.

CHAPTER 6

Equipment Modifications

CW communications have a fascination and charm not equalled by the oral mode, plus DX advantages and more certain contacts through QRM. Recently, the FCC assigned certain segments of the 50 MHz and 144 MHz bands to CW exclusively, which encourages code since (a) it will not be necessary to scout the entire band; (b) contacts are more certain to be made; (c) the operator will not feel that he may be interferring with a ragchew; and perhaps of greater importance (d) the technician will strive to attain the General Class license, thereby widening his field of experimentation.

The author has tried CW for some time but has found contacts few and at times interspersed with QSOs (vocal); however, now it is much easier to make a contact and maintain it without interruption.

CW on the HiBander

Let's consider changes to improve CW operation of the Hi-Bander. If one remains on crystal, the directions furnished by the manufacturer are quite satisfactory, although conversion from AM to CW and vice versa is awkward while in operation. With a VFO connected to the transmitter, considerable difficulty was encountered in obtaining an acceptable signal. Correspondence with the manufacturer provided suggestions, none of which was felt to be wholly applicable nor satisfactory.

The author, with the assistance of others, worked out the following changes. The experimentation is not finished, but it seems worthwhile to pass along the progress made with the hope some one will come up with a better idea. To be able to switch from AM to CW, with the VFO remaining in operation, required a DPDT switch connected as shown in Fig. 6-1.

Place the DPDT switch in the CW position and operate the Hi-Bander selector switch from Standby—CW; when the DPDT switch is at the AM position it operates from the Standby—AM. WARNING: Don't go on AM with the DPDT switch on CW or vice versa.

It was found necessary to insert a 10-mmf or a 15-mmf capacitor in the ground lead of the crystal socket as shown in

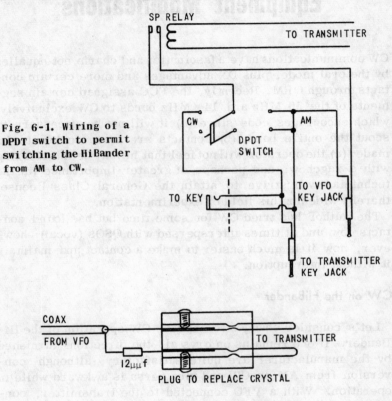

Fig. 6-1. Wiring of a DPDT switch to permit switching the Hi Bander from AM to CW.

Fig. 6-2. Diagram showing a capacitor in the crystal socket ground lead.

Fig. 6-2 when using the VFO on CW. Because the CW signal was measured and found to be poorly shaped due to key and impact effects and variable tone, a change in circuitry to provide corrective measures was employed. The jumper wire in Fig. 6-3 connects the cathode via the key to the ground. The wires that were cut were folded back in case a reconnection was needed.

The diagram is self explanatory; the actual change is simple, and after the chassis is removed from the cabinet requires about two minutes. A study of the HiBander circuit shows that a break in the cathode circuit at this point would not be likely to give a hot key. However, dry fingers across the terminals give no evidence of voltage, yet a voltmeter shows 140v. Further study should be made to determine the source and elimination of the voltage.

Aside from the rapid change in going from CW to AM during QSO (especially in checking each other's practice copy), it has been found that by using the key on the CW section in place of the selector switch one can very quickly and conveniently load the antenna without blowing fuses due to an excessive plate current. (Two hands on the knobs and an elbow on the key does

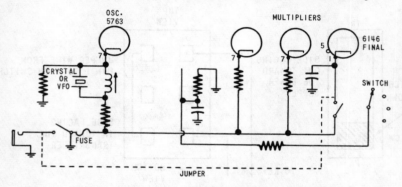

Fig. 6-3. Jumper for improving CW pulse shape.

the rapid-act trick). So someone, please, with an improvement on this improvement—CU on CW soon.

CW on the Gonset II

Almost everyone who owns or has owned a Gonset Communicator at one time or another wants to give CW a try, but feels that this is impossible. With the conversion shown in Fig. 6-4, it should be quite easy to send CW on the Gonset. When on CW, switch to "PA" and pull the mike out. On 'phone, return the mike and switch to "TR."

Double Conversion of the Gonset II Communicator

With activity on the 2 meter band increasing daily, it becomes more imperative for the receiver in use to display a reasonable amount of selectivity. Crowded band conditions, harmonic interference from aircraft, a tendency towards increased power and other similar disturbances have made reception of weaker stations practically impossible. It was for these reasons that it was decided to add double conversion to the Gonset II receiver.

The use of double conversion improves the image ratio and affords good selectivity in the IF amplifier. It is obtained in superheterodyne receivers by first converting the incoming signal to a rather high intermediate frequency, amplifying it, and then converting again, this time to a much lower frequency. The first intermediate frequency produces the neces-

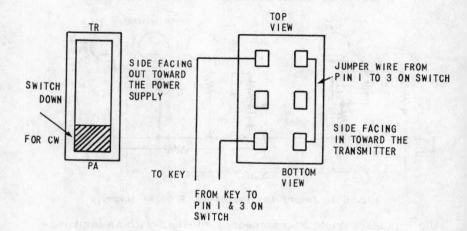

Fig. 6-4. Switch modifications for achieving CW transmission on the Gonset Communicator II.

sary separation between the image and the desired signal, while the second one supplies the desired selectivity.

The modification is simplicity in itself and well worth the time (about 1 hour) and the slight expense (about $5) involved. The 6 MHz signal, which is the output frequency of the first oscillator-mixer tube, appears at the grid of the 6BH6 (V11), the existing second IF amplifier. It is at this point that we inject the output of our added second local oscillator. Since this tube is now intended to operate as a mixer, it was found necessary to increase its bias. This was easily accomplished by changing the existing 120-ohm cathode resistor to 5000 ohms. The output of this stage is our new second intermediate frequency, and as such, necessitates replacing the two remaining 6MHz IF transformers with ones resonant to the new intermediate frequency. It was decided to use 455 kHz as the new intermediate frequency, since transformers of this frequency are relatively easy to obtain. A word of caution at this point: Since one of the replaced IF transformers is used for detector service, two identical transformers should not be used. An "input" type (similar to Miller Coil Co. No. 12-C1) can be used for the IF stage and an "output" type (similar to Miller No. 12-C2) can be used for the detector stage.

Chosen to generate the required local oscillator frequency was a modified Pierce circuit, utilizing a 6455 kHz crystal for excitation. The crystal frequency is not too critical and can be as much as 5 kHz either side of that frequency. Since the mixer stage employs cathode bias, the amount of injection voltage is non-critical; it is more important that an adequate amount be available. To insure this, it was necessary to tune the oscillator plate circuit with a peaking coil and a capacitor as indicated in the partial schematic diagram, Fig. 6-5. If desired, the capacitor used could be a trimmer. The tube chosen for the oscillator was a 12AT6, since these particular receivers are wired for 12-volt operation. A 6AT6 can be used in place of the 12AT6 for 6-volt receivers. B-plus voltage is obtained from the receiver B supply bus which feeds the plates and screens of the existing tubes.

The area adjacent to the RF amplifier, V8, located at the rear of the receiver chassis, was utilized for the oscillator circuit. The crystal socket and crystal was located outboard directly behind the oscillator tube. Tie points were inserted where required to support the parts of the oscillator circuit. After wiring the oscillator per the schematic, Fig. 6-5, oscillation can be determined by measuring the voltage at the grid pin (pin 1). If the circuit is oscillating, the voltage at this point will be approximately 3 to 4 volts negative. The wiring of the oscillator should present no problems since lead dress is not critical, but as in all good wiring practice, lead length should be kept to a minimum. All grounds should be returned to a single point, preferably at the oscillator socket.

If the oscillator is working, then the next step is to proceed to change the IF transformers. When lifting the existing components, remember that they will be returning to the same pin

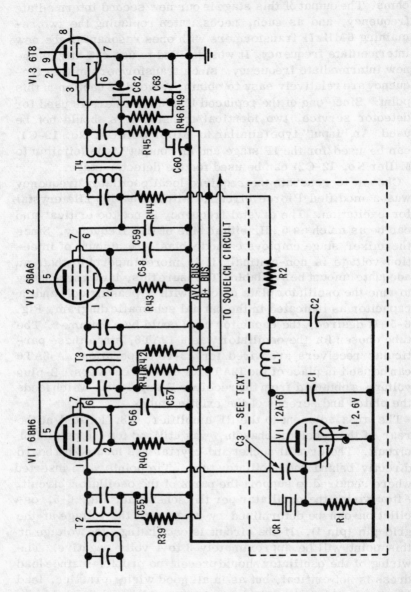

Fig. 6-5. Partial schematic of the Gonset II receiver. Notice the new oscillator circuit shown within the dashed lines and the reference designations which, except for those within the dashed box, conform to the Gonset schematic diagram.

of the new transformer; therefore, their lead dress should not be disturbed. After the new transformers have been installed, the job is completed by injecting the local oscillator energy to the new mixer grid (pin 1 of V11) by means of a "gimmick" coupling—in this case a 2.2-mmf ceramic capacitor was soldered directly to pin 1 of V11 and a short length of wire was soldered to the other end of the capacitor. The remaining wire end was then connected directly to pin 1 of the oscillator tube. It is important to keep this lead as short as possible to prevent coupling stray oscillator energy to existing circuits.

To align the two new transformers it is only necessary to peak them for maximum output, using either a station or existing background noise. No trouble was encountered during the conversion, so the job can be tackled with complete confidence

R39	270K 1/2W	T3*	455 kHz IF (input)
R40	5000 1/2W	T4*	455 kHz IF (output)
R41	10K 1W	C62	50 μμf ceramic
R42	220K 1/2W	C63	01 μf ceramic
R43	120K 1/2W	T2	6 MHz IF
R44	10K 1W		
R45	1.2 Meg 1/2W	Oscillator Circuit Parts List	
R46	1 Meg 1/2W		
R49	1 Meg 1/2W	CR1	6455 kHz Crystal (FT 243 type)
C55	.001 μf ceramic	R1	33K 1/2W Carbon
C56	.01 μf ceramic	R2	100K 1W carbon
C57	.01 μf ceramic	C1	50 μμf ceramic
C58	.01 μf ceramic	C2	01 μf ceramic
C59	.01 μf ceramic	L1	Peak. Coil, 500 μh
C60	.01 μf ceramic		(Miller 617 or equiv.)

*Originally 6 MHz

Parts list for Fig. 6-5.

towards a successful conclusion. The resulting sharpness and somewhat greater gain than before the conversion will certainly make worthwhile the money and effort expended.

Plate Modulating the Heath Seneca

I am one of the many amateurs who owns a Heathkit Seneca. When I purchased it, factory-built, the season's Sporadic E session was just beginning. After numerous successes, and after working 40 states on six, the DX subsided. To take its place, I realized a form of propagation called "extended groundwave." This is a condition which allows one to make contacts over a 150-mile or more distance under "dead band" conditions.

The Seneca's controlled-carrier screen grid modulation was ideal for Es, good auroras, and average groundwave. However, when extended groundwave signals became weak and my own signal diminished in strength to only one "S" unit out of the noise, the audio proved to be almost unreadable. Under similar conditions, the audio proved to be 100% on full plate modulation and signals were Q4 and Q5. For this reason I feel that owners of Senecas can be greatly aided in making groundwave and aurora contacts by converting to plate modulation.

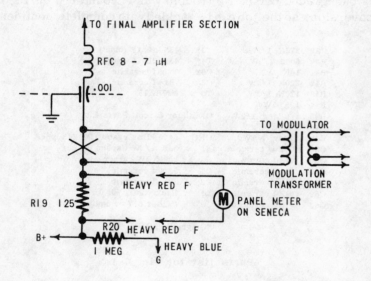

Fig. 6-6. Remove the wire at "X" and connect the modulation transformer in series with the lead carrying the B+.

I use an Eico 730 modulator-driver to achieve plate modulation using the circuit shown in Fig. 6-6. Upon testing, I found that stations I had worked previously now gave me reports of my modulation being "100% better" than before the conversion. Any modulator delivering 50 watts of audio may be used. Once installed, merely place the Seneca's function switch in the CW position, apply B plus to the modulator, and you're in business. Since no change has been made in the Seneca's original modulation system, the resale value remains high.

Customizing the Heath Sixer

After working with my Sixer from the day of its completion, I am prone to say that this little lunchpail is probably one of the finest pieces of gear a beginning six meter man can obtain. I say this not because of its operation, which has been said to leave much to be desired, but because of the opportunities it gives for a green ham to experiment on his rig and learn the strings of practical electronics. I have done all the work on my rig myself, with the aid of a neighbor's electric drill.

1. The first change incorporated was in the power supply filtering system. I substituted 3-henry, 50 ma filter chokes for the two resistors R401 and R402. They can be mounted subchassis, one between the two audio tube sockets, 6AQ5 and 12AX7; the other is mounted to the rear of the audio volume control. These chokes can be bought for under 50¢ apiece from one of the small stores advertising in any of the current ham magazines. These chokes, by the way, raise the plate voltage on the receiver and speech amplifier, resulting in higher gain.

2. Another alteration which is more than necessary in many Sixers is the elimination of transmitter instability. The reason for the drifting is the oscillator. The oscillator tank circuit uses as a capacitor the interelectrode capacitance of the triode section. As the tube warms up, the frequency drifts around the center frequency and finally settles down when the tubes settle down. The ill was cured by putting a 2-μμf capacitor across the oscillator coil (1-201) and shorting out enough coil turns to have the tank tune to six meters again.

3. In order to facilitate tuning, two changes are in order. First, cut a hole in the case directly over the oscillator coil so it can be tuned from outside the case with a tuning rod. The final can be tuned the same way, or if you wish not to fish around in a dark box for a little screw, it can be altered for front tuning; remove the final tank capacitor (C-208) and the final coil slug, which screws right out. Secure a small variable capacitor and place it between the T-R switch and the end of the chassis. Mount the capacitor with the tuning screw

coming through the chassis face. Connect the stator plates to the plate of the tube (pin 9). The other plates (the rotors) are connected to ground. With this arrangement the transmitter can be tuned with the case in place; also the neon bulb can be observed more clearly.

4. While we're on the transmitter section, I'd like to include a change I made for work at my summer QTH. I have no six meter antenna there, so I am forced to use the TV antenna system. The present loading capacitor, however, does not accommodate the 300-ohm impedance setup with full output, so I replaced it with a 140-μμf air-dielectric variable capaci-

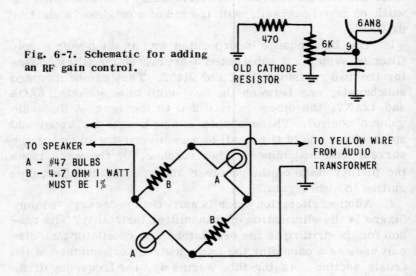

Fig. 6-7. Schematic for adding an RF gain control.

Fig. 6-8. Schematic of an inexpensive squelch circuit.

tor (screw type, also). This is neither an important nor necessary change, but if work with a variety of antennas is anticipated, it might come in handy.

5. I have found, incidentally, that a tube shield left ungrounded on the transmitter tube allows for a slight increase in input power. The heavier the shield, the larger the increase. I started out with a small tube shield and soldered over 20 pieces of #10 wire on it to dissipate heat and wound up with a wierd, porcupine-looking monstrosity. However, since my rig draws in excess of 45 ma cathode current, unmodulated, I need it.

6. The transmitter conversion enabled me to raise the input from 4 1/2 watts to 10 watts! Just put a 10 microhenry 50 ma RF choke across the transmitter grid resistor (R203) and retune.

7. I'd like to pass along some tube changes also. The 6AU8 transmitter tube can be directly replaced by a higher current 6CX8, while the 12AX7 can be just as easily replaced by a 5751 hi-fi tube. I have found by experimentation that the 6CX8 draws more current than either the 6AU8 or 6AU8A and would recommend it above the others.

8. About every Sixer owner I have had a QSO with has a complaint about the lack of receiver selectivity. This can be remedied as easily as placing a 2.7 meg 1/2 watt resistor across the capacitor (C111) and retuning the detector coil. The increase in selectivity is usually noticed on the stronger sig-

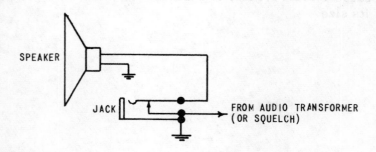

Fig. 6-9. Diagram showing headphone jack addition.

nals, but a slight overall decrease in bandwidth will be noticed.

9. A little tinkering on my part brought a desire to add an RF gain control to the receiver. I tried a few ways but none seemed to work as well as I wanted it to. The best way so far is to remove the 470-ohm cathode resistor (R102) and substitute a 6K potentiometer. Connect one end of the pot to ground and the slider to the cathode of the receiver RF amplifier tube. The control can be mounted between the volume control and mike connector with a small knob to fit the space. See Fig. 6-7.

10. Next in order comes some audio stage refinements. First, the addition of a squelch circuit sold commercially for $5.98 and which costs about 75¢ to build. See Fig. 6-8.

11. Headphones always come in handy on any rig, including

the Sixer. For the headphone operation, put a jack in as illustrated in Fig. 6-9.

12. Here's a sneaky way to get MCW out of the Heathkit job. Put a headphone jack on the rear chassis apron in the space between the two screw legs next to the power plug. Some case cutting is also in order here. Connect the ungrounded end of the jack to the audio transformer secondary lead that goes below the chassis. With the transmitter on, place your mike near the speaker, and key. The audio feedback produces a strong piercing note. If you have a squelch circuit in the rig, you may have to short it out to obtain sufficient feedback, or, better yet, put a switch in for the squelch circuit.

13. Finally, we come to the last change, and a minor one at that. I replaced the antenna connector with a UHF coax connector which fits right in place. I used a UHF coax socket because I could not install a regular coax connector in view of its size.

CHAPTER 7

VFO Projects for VHF

The common practice in building a variable-frequency oscillator for the 50-MHz hand is to use the sixth harmonic of a conventional 8-MHz tunable oscillator. However, the sixth harmonic is of a rather high order and difficulties begin to develop. For example, when we multiply our 8-MHz signal six times, we also multiply any drift it may have by the same factor. Consequently, if our 8-MHz oscillator drifts 100 Hz, then the sixth harmonic (which we are utilizing at 50 MHz) will have drifted 600 Hz, ad infinitum. Also, many tunable oscillators will change frequency slightly during standby periods (again multiplying by six). This is not good, particularly if you drift under that rockcrushing signal up the band.

A Stable 50-MHz VFO

The crowded band conditions and highly selective receivers in use on six meters today make a stable VFO a necessity. The ideal system would be to maintain the stability of this basic 8-MHz oscillator at 50 MHz. How can we do this without multiplying? Simple. We can heterodyne it up to 50 MHz—the same process your converter uses, only in reverse. Now if we place our tunable oscillator at, say, 9 MHz and heterodyne it against a 41-MHz signal—the stability of which can be assured by making it crystal controlled—you will have the product of these two signals, 50 MHz. A little care is called for at this point, however, as the difference or image signal at 32 MHz (41 minus 9) will also be present. Adequate selectivity between the mixer and the final amplifier will attenuate this image signal sufficiently so that it will not pose any problem. With this heterodyne VFO we can also solve the problem of standby drift simply by leaving the 9-MHz tunable oscillator on continuously and turning off the 41-MHz oscillator during standy periods.

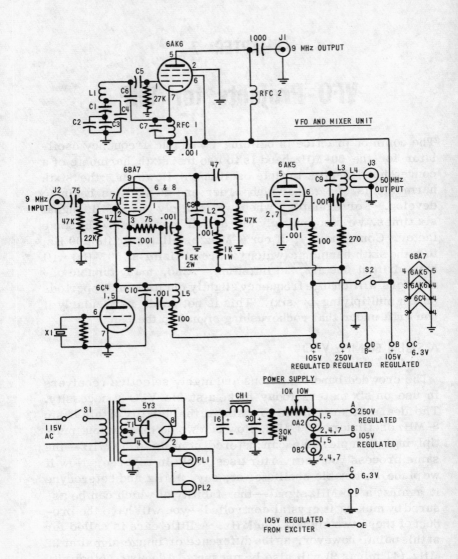

Fig. 7-1. A 50-MHz VFO circuit, designed with an eye to ultimate stability. Output is at 6 meters. Power supply is shown separately in case a stable source is already available.

In leaving the tunable oscillator on continuously, however, we must select a frequency range for it that will not fall in line with any harmonics that might land in the 6-meter band; otherwise, we will have to contend with an annoying signal on the receiver and it·may clobber up a weak DX station. The 9-MHz range meets this requirement quite nicely.

The VFO in Fig. 7-1 was built with the aforementioned points in mind and worked out quite well in daily use at the author's QTH during the past year, both on phone and CW. The tunable oscillator uses a 6AK6 in the tried-and-proven Clapp oscillator circuit. A 6C4 is used in the crystal oscillator with a third overtone 41-MHz crystal. The mixer is a 6BA7 penta-grid converter tube. The output from the tunable oscillator is fed into the signal grid and the output from the crystal os-

C1	100 μμf zero temperature coef. ceramic	L3	8 t B & W 3003
C2	Cardwell unit	L4	1 t link on cold end of L3
C3	2 plate midget variable	L5	9 t B & W 3003
C4	250 μμf silver mica	RFC 1, 2	2.5 mh RF choke
C5	100 μμf zero temperature coef. ceramic	X1	41 MHz third overtone crystal
C6, 7	270 μμf zero temperature coef. ceramic	S1	SPST toggle switch
		S2	SPST spring loaded "push to make" switch
C8, 9	20 μμf midget variable	T1	Power transformer 300/300 at 60 ma 5V at 2 amps. 6.3 V at 2 amps.
C10	20 μμf glass piston		
L1	See text	CH1	Filter choke, 10 hy at 60 ma
L2	5 t B & W 3003	PL 1, 2	No. 47 pilot lamp

Parts list for Fig. 7-1.

cillator is coupled in to the injection grid. The 50-MHz output from the mixer drives a 6AK5 straight-through buffer amplifier. The output from the buffer is adequate to drive a 2E26 over a 500-kHz range of the six meter band without the necessity of retuning.

A Cardwell tuning capacitor and associated gear drive is used to tune the variable-frequency oscillator. This unit has approximately the same capacitor and drive assembly as used in the LM and BC-221 frequency meters and it is just about the best unit you can use in a VFO. Needless to say, these units are a bit expensive new, so if you don't want to make this worthwhile investment in a tuning capacitor and drive assembly, I would suggest purchasing a tuning capacitor and gear train from an ARC-5 transmitter. These are quite common on the

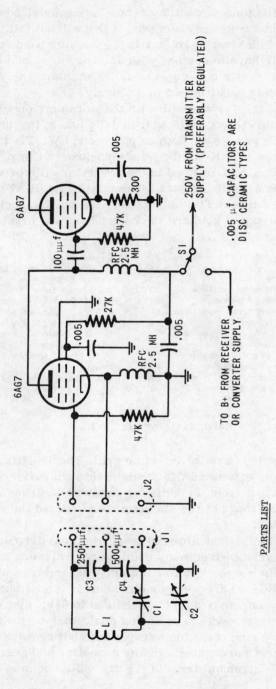

Fig. 7-2. Schematic of the 6AG7 VFO.

PARTS LIST

C1   100 μμf variable
C2   15 μμf variable
C2, C4   Preferably silver mica

250V FROM TRANSMITTER
SUPPLY (PREFERABLY REGULATED)

.005 μf CAPACITORS ARE
DISC CERAMIC TYPES

TO B+ FROM RECEIVER
OR CONVERTER SUPPLY

6AG7

6AG7

100 μμf

.005

300

47K

RFC
2.5 MH

S1

27K

.005

.005

RFC
2.5 MH

47K

J2

J1

C3
250 μμf

C4
500 μμf

C1

C2

L1

100

surplus market at reasonable prices and will give a good account of themselves in this application. The tuning range of this particular unit was restricted to 9.0 to 9.5 MHz, which naturally restricted the output frequency range to 50.0 to 50.5 MHz. This, along with the 50:1 gear reduction of the Cardwell unit, provided a very large amount of bandspread and, consequently, very easy tuning. If you want the VFO to cover more or all of the six meter band, there are two ways this can be accomplished; the frequency range of the tunable oscillator can be increased at the sacrifice of bandspread, or far better, crystal switching in 500-kHz steps can be used. Thus, by switching over to a 41.5 MHz crystal in the crystal oscillator, the output frequency range of the VFO would be 50.5 to 51.0 MHz while the tunable oscillator would still be tuning its basic frequency range of 9.0 to 9.5 MHz. The oscillator coil (L1) should be a high Q inductor. The shielded

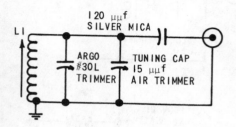

Fig. 7-3. Circuit of the "quickie" tubeless VFO. Use a short piece of RG-58/U cable to connect to the crystal socket.

PARTS LIST

L1   17 turns #22 wire on a 3/8" slug-tuned coil form. Green or red slug is OK.

slug tuned coil from a BC-459 command transmitter was used in this VFO. This coil is wound on a ribbed ceramic form and works out quite well.

There is nothing very critical or tricky in building this VFO. Just make sure that all oscillator components are mounted rigidly and keep leads short and use heavy wire. By exercising a little judgment in circuit layout, you should not have any difficulties. Power supplies for both oscillators should be well regulated.

A 6AG7-Type VFO

Building a VFO for our VHF bands that meets with present

stability standards is no easy task. Extreme care has to be taken to avoid any variation of geometrical dimensions of the frequency-determining components. The slightest drift produced in this way will be multiplied in the following doubler or tripler stages and appear magnified at the output frequency. This is why 50 MHz seems to be the highest frequency at which it is safe to use this normal approach of VFO control. It is better to use the heterodyne principle, well known from SSB techniques, when you plan to go to 144, 220, or 432 MHz.

The circuit used is the popular Clapp oscillator, shown in

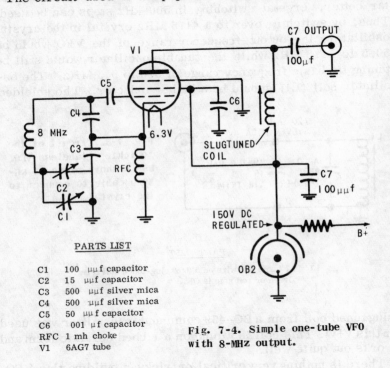

PARTS LIST

C1	100 μμf capacitor
C2	15 μμf capacitor
C3	500 μμf silver mica
C4	500 μμf silver mica
C5	50 μμf capacitor
C6	001 μf capacitor
RFC	1 mh choke
V1	6AG7 tube

Fig. 7-4. Simple one-tube VFO with 8-MHz output.

Fig. 7-2. As can be seen, the tuned circuit is a separate unit and was mounted on a different chassis. This is of great advantage, as you now can place this vital part of the VFO away from any heat-generating element, and adding to this a careful selection of good quality parts and solid mechanical construction, the final result is real first class stability. The connection between the tuned circuit and the oscillator tube is made by two pieces of RG 59/U coax, three or four feet long and taped in parallel. The two shields are soldered together at both ends, while the two inner conductors are needed to connect the grid and cathode of the 6AG7 to the top and midpoint, respectively, of the voltage divider formed by C3 and C4.

In my case, the oscillator is working on 6.25 MHz, while the plate of the second 6AG7 shown is tuned to 12.5 MHz. Following this are two 6CL6s, doubling the frequency in the first stage to 25 and in the second to 50 MHz, which drives the 5894 final. The plate circuits of the three doubler tubes use little air trimmers and are stagger tuned, so the VFO can be tuned to any frequency in the first 500-kHz portion of the 6 meter band without the need to touch any other control. The resulting speed in frequency changing is of great convenience in contest work or when you want to answer a DX station's call just a few seconds before your local competitors are also on the right spot. Switch S1 permits one to power the oscillator from the receiver supply while listening, permitting a check of your own frequency or to zero-beat another without putting the transmitter on the air.

Coil L1 has 19 turns of No. 16 wire, 1 3/4 inches in diameter and nearly 2 inches long. The turns are cemented to 3 solid lucite strips, one of which is supported by two heavy 1 1/4-inch feed-through insulators. C2, the bandspread capacitor, should be of the best quality. I used a Hammarlund HF-15X which was on hand. Band-setting capacitor C1 was mounted below the chassis. If you put this unit into a cabinet, take care to make it large enough so that any metal surface stays at least 2 inches away from the coil; otherwise, the Q of the coil will be lowered.

Capacitors C3 and C4 were soldered on the terminals of connector J1. Any vernier dial will work fine, but be careful to avoid any strain on the shaft of C2; a flexible coupling would be convenient. The finished unit is mounted on four little rubber grommets to prevent any vibration that might influence the frequency-determining circuit.

Once everything is mounted, check the right setting of the band-setting capacitor C1 with a GDO (grid dip meter). If there are no wiring errors, this is about the only thing you have to do. If you wish to use miniature tubes throughout, just replace the 6AG7 tubes with 6CL6s. It also would be possible to change the resonant frequency to 8.4 MHz and tune the plate circuit of the second 6AG7 to 25 MHz, reaching the

6 meter band with one stage less. Stability will probably be the same.

Figs. 7-3 and 7-4 show a tubeless and a one-tube VFO. Employing only a 6AG7, the inexpensive VFO is quite stable if the incoming voltage is well filtered. Any supply voltage fluctuation will be noticeable in the final operating stability of the unit.

CHAPTER 8

Receiver and Modulator Circuits

In all ham shacks there is always a need for a second receiver when converters are used to cover the VHF bands. Some hams have arranged for their converters to be changed by flipping a switch, while others must do it manually. As a result, this latter ham seldom changes his converters in order to tune the other VHF bands and thereby misses out on some good contacts. An ideal solution to this problem would be to have a receiver for each converter, with the best receiver connected to the converter covering the band most in use. Such a setup permits a good check on the bands every time you are in the ham shack. This may sound too far-fetched and expensive, but actually it isn't.

The Second Receiver

At present there is a receiver on the surplus market that would be ideal for a setup like this. It is the BC 603, which in its original state is designed for FM and presently is selling for $15 to $20 at most. The modifications for AM were covered in CQ Magazine and reprints of this article are available. The receiver is manually tuned or has 10 pushbuttons. The tuning range is 20-27.9 MHz and the receiver has a panel-mounted speaker. By using a 40-MHz crystal in your 2-meter converter, the IF output would be 24-28 MHz. The M.A.R.S. frequency falls at 23.46 MHz. Using a 40-MHz crystal in your 1 1/4-meter converter and using the fifth harmonic, the IF would be 20-25 MHz. For 6 meters a 30-MHz crystal is needed for 20-24 MHz, and even the 3/4 meter converter offers direct calibration by tuning 22-23 MHz. The one fault with this receiver is the method used for manual tuning which requires the use of the thumb.

It is indeed a pleasure to be able to operate on one band and

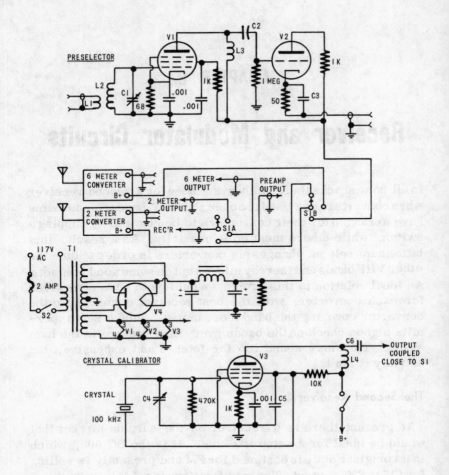

PARTS LIST

L1	3 turns of #20 wire 1" diameter, 1/8" from bottom of L2	C5	140 μμf
		C6	20 μμf
L2	7 turns of #20 wire 1" diameter part of B & W 3015 Miniductor	S1	1 section, 2 pole, 4 positions
L3, 4	1.1 mh RF choke	S2, 3	SPST toggle switch
C1	130 μμf midget variable capacitor	T1	Stancor PM-8407 or an equivalent
C2	.001 μf	V1	6DE6
C3	.01	V2	6C4
C4	7 to 45 μμf trimmer	V3	6AU6
		V4	5U4

7 X 12 X 3" aluminum box or any available chassis.
RCA phono plugs and jacks, knobs, hardware, etc.

Fig. 8-1. Schematic of the "combine," a method for achieving maximum in 6- and 2-meter reception flexibility with a minimum of effort.

be able to listen to the other bands at the same time, especially when things are happening or you expect them to. It is very easy to tap off some of the IF signal of the BC 603 and feed it into the main receiver if more selectivity is desired. Why not try one and see for yourself?

Preselector Plus Converters for 6 and 2 Meters

The gadget described below is for the ham who likes to switch from low frequencies to VHF with a minimum of effort. This particular unit consists of two converters, for 6 and 2 meters, a 14- to 30-MHz preselector, a crystal calibrator, and a complete power supply. See Fig. 8-1. The preselector can also be used as an IF amplifier with any of the converters. The layout is simple and straightforward and no difficulty should be encountered in building this unit. The original preselector consisted of two tubes, but due to the fact that a crystal calibrator was needed, one was removed. The wiring is not critical and most parts can be found in your junkbox. The combine was built on a 7" x 12" x 3" aluminum chassis, but any chassis is sufficient as long as it holds securely whatever you want on it. The converters that I used were printed-circuit types, so the holes in the chassis had to be large enough to accommodate each converter. No special tools were used to cut the chassis holes, except an electric drill and a file. A lot of elbow grease was used this way, but it was well worth it!

Coils L1 and L2 are made from a 10-turn length of B&W Miniductor. L1 consists of three turns and L2 of seven turns. Unwind 1/4 of a turn from each end of the coils. When cutting the wire, be sure not to cut the insulation. In this manner the insulation will hold the coils together.

V1 is a 6DE6, which has a slightly lower noise level than the conventional 6CB6. V2 is a 6C4 which is used as a cathode follower. When using the 6DE6 alone, the gain is much sharper and you have to peak C1 each time you tune to another frequency. With the 6C4 you tend to draw out the gain over the whole band and C1 can be left in one place.

To use the preselector as an IF amplifier will depend on what IF your converters are feeding into. If it is between 14 to 30 MHz, there is no problem. If the frequency is lower, you will have to increase the number of turns on L1 and L2. Only ex-

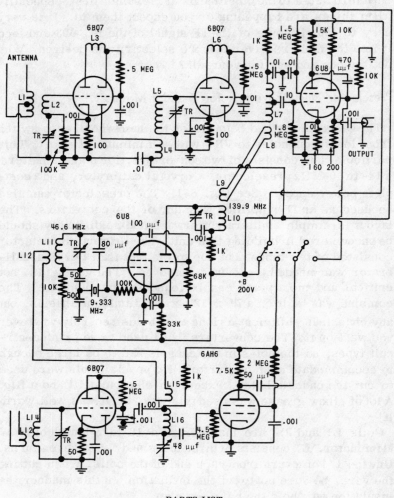

PARTS LIST

L1	4 turns			L10	2 turns - ∅ 9	μμf
L2	7 turns - ∅ 6	μμf		L11	8 turns - ∅ 9	μμf
L3	5 turns - ∅ 6	μμf		L12	2 turns	
L4	2 turns - ∅ 6	μμf		L13	2 turns	
L5	4 turns - ∅ 6	μμf		L14	9 turns - ∅ 12	μμf
L6	5 turns - ∅ 6	μμf		L15	2 turns	
L7	4 turns - ∅ 6	μμf		L16	7 turns - ∅ 12	μμf
L8	2 turns					
L9	2 turns			Tr	3-30 μμf trimmer	

Fig. 8-2. Schematic of the single-crystal "2N6" converter.

perimentation will determine the correct coils for your particular IF. To connect your converter to the preselector, merely run a short piece of coax from the output terminals of your converter to the input terminals of the preselector. You may have to readjust your converter's output slug or trimmer after connecting them together.

The crystal calibrator is simple in design, and the only difficulty that will arise is getting the 100-kHz crystal cheap. A 6AU6 is used as the oscillator, but other similar tubes could be used without altering the circuit too much. I have also included here a switching circuit that enables me to switch from converter to converter without any difficulty.

A "2N6" Converter with One Crystal

The following is a description of a converter for the two lower VHF bands. Its principal characteristic is the use of only one local oscillator unit, controlled by a single crystal, for both bands. In this case, the resulting intermediate frequency is 3.33 to 7.33 MHz for the 6 meter band and 4.0 to 8.0 MHz for 2 meters, and the tuning is done on an HRO receiver. Applying B-plus voltage to all tubes of the converter makes it possible to tune both VHF bands simultaneously, a very convenient possibility for local work. When searching for DX, one of the mixers is disconnected, eliminating the noise contribution of the second channel. Image rejection is, of course, not the best with such a low intermediate frequency, but this caused no problem here. In fact it was considered advantageous as it permits one to keep an eye on the signals around 43 MHz, which gives an idea of how high the MUF is coming up.

The circuit of the converter, shown in Fig. 8-2, may be broken up into the following three parts: The 2-meter RF channel with its mixer and cathode follower, the local oscillator unit, and the 6-meter RF amplifier and mixer. Two cascode stages are connected in series to amplify the 144-MHz signals before they are applied to the mixer section (pentode) of the 6U8. At the input circuit the tuning capacitor is in series with the grid-cathode capacitance of the tube, which allows the use of a larger coil and better coupling conditions. Notice also the high-value screen dropping resistor used at the mixer; it markedly lowers the noise of this tube. The triode section of the 6U8 is the cathode-follower for both the 6-meter and 2-meter mixers.

The oscillator circuit employs a 9.33-kHz crystal oscillating at its fifth overtone. The triode section of the 6U8 acts as a tripler, bringing the frequency to 140 MHz, and it is now coupled through a small link to the 2-meter mixer. At the same time, the 46.6-MHz energy from the overtone oscillator is coupled to the grid circuit of the 6AH6, which acts as mixer for the 6-meter signals. Here again screen grid voltage is supplied through a high-value resistor to lower the noise level of this tube. The 6-meter RF stage is a normal cascode, employing also a 6BQ7.

Two small U-shaped chassis were screwed together, one of them supporting the 6-meter RF stage and mixer and the other one the rest of the circuit. The different resonant circuits should first be adjusted approximately with the help of a grid-dip meter, and then in actual operation to the owners preference—i.e., for more or less uniform response over the entire band or peaked for maximum gain on a certain portion of the band. The adjustment of the overtone oscillator should pose no problem and more detailed information about this subject can be found in the ARRL Handbook.

Four-Tube Modulator

This modulator incorporates several unusual features:

- Only four inexpensive tubes
- No modulation transformer necessary
- Negative peak clipping
- Inverse feedback for fidelity

The circuits are exactly what I use in the station and I'm sure more could be squeezed out of the basic design if someone tried. The third part is an attempt to reduce an extremely complicated study to a simple qualitative exposition. It is by no means all encompassing and is completely untried as far as mathematical analysis is concerned.

The Preamp

This portion of the overall circuit (Fig. 8-3) is of quite conventional design. Probably the most important comments I could make would be those pertaining to practical considerations to keep in mind during the actual construction. First, remember that any microphone amplifier is intrinsically a high gain one, and certain precautions must be followed in order that the usual problems be avoided. Among these are included: (a) the necessity of shielding the tube, (b) the importance of short leads, and (c) the problems of lead dress. Tube shielding is important for two reasons, both of which are commonly known: hum reduction and the elimination of RF pickup leading to the familiar "howl." Most of the relatively uninitiated tend to forget about the short lead problem and as a result are plagued with RF feedback. The principle to remember here is that all vacuum tubes are sufficiently non-

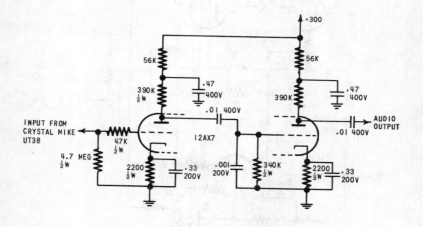

Fig. 8-3. The preamplifier section of the modulator.

linear to produce detection of RF signals, and a lead of only a few inches has very definite radiation resistance characteristics which serve as an antenna—especially at 50 MHz and above. The remaining point is the capacitive coupling which may occur between these leads and the high signal level of the output. High audio frequency feedback can cause oscillations at supersonics, which will produce intermodulation products difficult to identify in the absence of proper equipment. The preceding remarks are quite as appropos to lead dress as to lead length, and the only additional admonition to be added is that concerning the microphone input. Wherever possible, one should attempt a layout which will place the microphone input

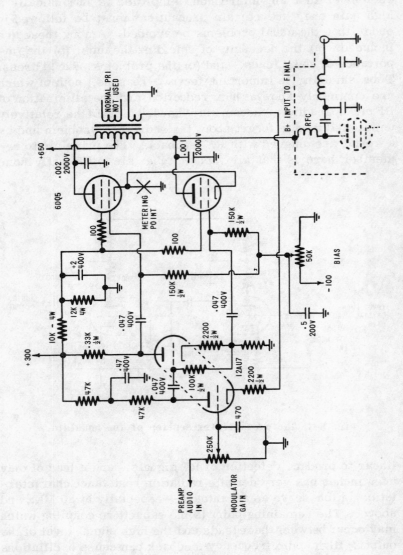

Fig. 8-4. Power amplifier section of the modulator.

on an opposite side of the chassis with respect to the modula-
lation output.

The Power Amplifier

Let us begin by listing those design criteria which became
practical goals.

- Must be simple to build
- Should be high efficiency
- Fidelity should be acceptable
- Some form of clipping should be provided
- The power output should be high
- Cost should be minimized

The simplicity factor became the number of components required. I suppose this could be reduced, but it seemed that
a triode alloted to phase inversion was perhaps somewhat
easier to accommodate than a separate transformer. Simplicity, in my mind, is really associated with efficiency in
that the use of high gm tubes in the output stage permits the
elimination of power drivers. The actual electrical efficiency
is designed high by the use of near Class B operation of the
6DQ5 tubes, which eliminates the idling current of these tubes
representing purely unrecoverable loss.

Fidelity in amateur transmitters is a rather nebulous thing,
and everyone has his own definition. My own requires that
low frequencies be suppressed to some extent; however, the
frequency response here is extended to full range, and any distortion is automatically reduced by the use of the negative
voltage feedback. This negative feedback tends to extend the
frequency response of the power amplifier over a broad bandwidth, and my recommendation is to limit the response of the
preamp to that subjectively desired.

Since this is a direct-coupled scheme, the instantaneous voltage at the output terminals cannot drop appreciably below the
"knee" of the modulation output tubes. The knee is defined as
the point on the $e_p - i_p$ characteristic curve where the plate
curve leaves diode operation and becomes pentode. Thus, the
supply voltage to the RF final can never go completely to zero
and the resulting modulation cannot be greater in the downward
direction than about 95%, which gives effective high-level clipping.

There are two important parameters to be considered in producing a high power output:

1. The actual location of the knee (should be as low in voltage as possible).
2. The peak current that can be drawn through the output tube.

Inspection of a tube manual will show that the 6DQ5 qualifies well in both categories with a knee voltage of about 50 volts and a peak current of nearly an ampere when operated with about 175 volts on the screen. Although the output has never been measured directly, I have calculated about 150 watts for these operating conditions.

The remaining goal is the cost factor. All amateurs are confronted with this limitation at some time or other, and one of the prime causes is the cost of the modulation transformer. A modulation transformer capable of 100 watts of audio power becomes a difficult and expensive procurement problem. My own solution to this one is the use of a 60-Hz power transformer obtained from an old RCA television receiver of about 1947 vintage or so, the old 621 series which was the 7-inch picture tube. I was always impressed with the amount of iron and the relatively great amount of copper used in the design of such transformers, and upon trial was very well satisfied with the performance obtained. Inspection of Fig. 8-4 shows that the transformer utilizes the normal secondary (high-voltage winding) as the main one with the normal primary (117v) and the rectifier filament windings unused. If the designer wishes, he may use the conventional primary as an auxilliary modulator by tying it in series with the screen of the RF final. Further ingenuity may dictate other usage such as retrieval of the normal rectifier filament winding for some sort of modulation indicator utilization. The important factor here is that a high power modulator transformer may be obtained for relatively little cost (sometimes as low as $5.00, or perhaps free if the owner is sufficiently sold on cleaning out the cellar of that "junk"). Other TV receivers will yield perhaps even higher power modulation transformers.

The cost of replacement was certainly a considerable factor in the choice of tubes used in this design. It was felt that the large volume of receiving tubes would always result in lower cost and easier procurement.

Let's mention some miscellaneous practical items at this

point. The bias should be adjusted so that a current meter inserted into the common cathode metering point will read in the vicinity of 20 ma. This value is not critical and is left to the option of the builder. If adjusted in excess of 80 ma, the plate dissipation of the 6DQ5s will be exceeded, but if the meter reads less than about 10 ma, the overall gain will be reduced. The voltages listed are quite tolerable and the B values indicated are more or less minimum. Variations of the 300v supply of 20% higher will cause little change in the performance of the circuit. Variation of the +650v supply will

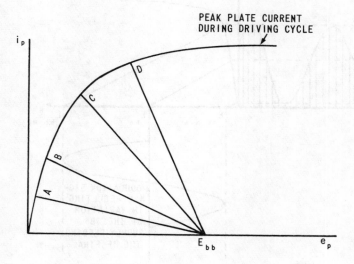

Fig. 8-5. Drawing a load line on a tube character-istic. Here, the load is reflected back upon the output final.

change only the power output. Normal tolerance for all com-ponents should be no tighter than ±10%, with most components variable to ±20%.

As for my own personal usage, this circuit has been my main transmitter modulator for the last 2 1/2 years and is currently being operated modulating finals of 100 watts input on 6 and 100 meters and up to 180 watts input on the bands between. The RF efficiency of these finals is in the neighborhood of 70%. I seldom am asked to increase my modulation even though my signal may be weak (on long groundwave, for example) and almost never have I had a complaint of splatter. This circuit has been used only with home-brew transmitters, although I feel an ideal application would be for use with a Senaca.

General Discussion About Plate Modulation

While we're on the general subject of plate modulation, per-

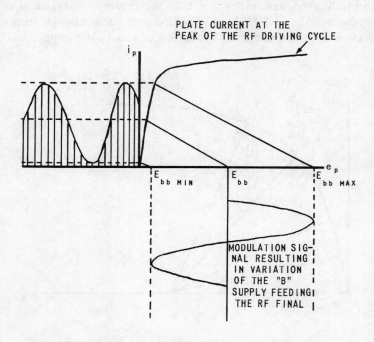

Fig. 8-6. Phone condition with the supply voltage point varying dynamically between the limits of the modulating waveform. Here, good 98% modulation is shown with antenna matched to final tube for maximum transfer of power.

haps it would be in order to compose a brief dissertation on the general theory. The description to follow is admittedly an oversimplification, but seems to me to give a fair qualitative analysis.

Most everyone has studied the technique of drawing a load line on a tube characteristic and developing certain conclusions. Let us now consider this tool in explaining the action of plate modulation. See Fig. 8-5. The load reflected upon the plate of the RF final from the antenna (if the match is good between the antenna and the transmission line) is purely resistive. Let us assume this condition, the condition representing good match between the tube and the antenna feed line (best loading) is that labeled as (b). This is the condition best fitting the requirements of 'phone operation where 100% modulation is desired. Good operation for CW may be obtained for lower output resistances and the slope may be steepened to (c) for this form of emission. The limiting parameter here is plate dissipation. The lines (a) and (d) represent the re-

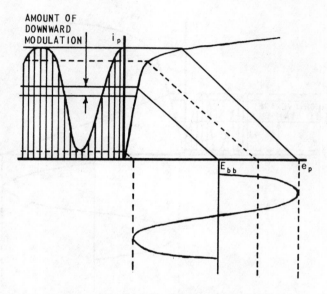

Fig. 8-7. Graphic demonstration of a condition where final is loaded too heavily.

maining extremes—(a) the case for insufficient loading where the power input is low, a condition restricting the radiated power; and (d) the case where the output is coupled too tightly into the final, resulting in lots of input power but poor efficiency.

Let us now re-examine the 'phone condition described by load line (b). We find in Fig. 8-6 the same drawing, but with the supply voltage point varying dynamically between the limits of the modulating waveform. Notice that the slope of the load line does not change; rather, it moves back and forth just as if the supply voltage were varying (which in fact is happening). As long as the load line intercepts the characteristic curve below the knee, linear modulation will occur. For the case where the stated conditions are met, the cyclic increase is exactly equal to the cyclic decrease in plate current and the average plate current does not change.

Fig. 8-7 shows the condition where the final is loaded too heavily (represented by the steep load line mentioned previously.) Here we have the same original conditions prevailing in all respects, except the slope of the load line is

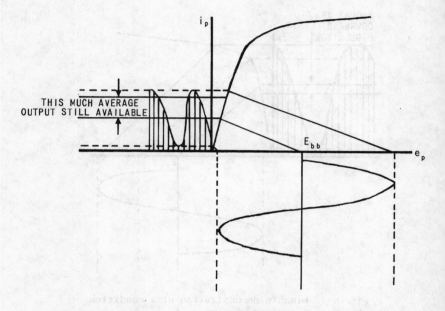

Fig. 8-8. Illustration of too-light loading. Antenna load undercoupled.

increased and the peak of the modulating cycle runs the plate current over the knee of the curve. Now, the tube cannot supply the increase in plate current called for by the modulator and the positive swing is rounded off. The result is that the average current decreases with modulation and "downward" modulation prevails, as well as the introduction of heavy distortion. If output loading is too light, the condition pictured in Fig. 8-8 is descriptive and nothing more serious than reduced output occurs. (However, this assumes nothing else changes.) From a practical standpoint, regulation of voltage, both DC and audio, may allow arcing and perhaps splatter with conventional modulators.

Modulator for Discriminating VHF'ers

After operating for more than a year on the VHF band with transmitters in the 100-watt class, I began to consider the possibility of changing to higher power. Much time was spent with paper and pencil figuring out the economical side of several suitable designs, but the final sum was always well above my financial possibilities. So some other method had to be used to increase the "talk power" of the existing trans-mitter setup, and the natural approach was to use a speech clipper in the modulator. (A more radical and modern method would have been to throw out the carrier for DSB, and per-haps one sideband—for SSB, but this step was left for a little later.)

Fig. 8-9 shows the circuit of the complete modulator, with-out power supplies. The audio output of the microphone is amplified in a conventional 2-stage amplifier before going through the series-clipper circuit, which works very well even at heavy clipping without introducing phase rotations. The following triode amplifier compensates the voltage loss in the preceding clipper stage, and in its plate circuit you will find a low-pass filter with a cut-off frequency at around 3000 Hz. Such a filter has to follow every clipper circuit, be-cause clipping means distortion, distortion means high-fre-quency components (harmonics), and these high-frequency components should be removed before they reach the modu-lator stage and generate splatter, increasing the channel width used by the transmission without adding anything to the intel-ligibility. The filter shown has to be terminated by a 3,000-ohm resistor; otherwise, it will not work properly.

The potentiometer at the grid side of the following amplifier tube will control the modulation level in final operation, while the one at the input side (after the first pentode stage) will con-trol the clipping level. Some negative feedback was used in the driver stage to lower the plate resistance of the 6F6 and provide better regulation when the grids of the modulator tubes swing into the positive region and draw grid current. The usual precautions should be taken to avoid oscillation in these

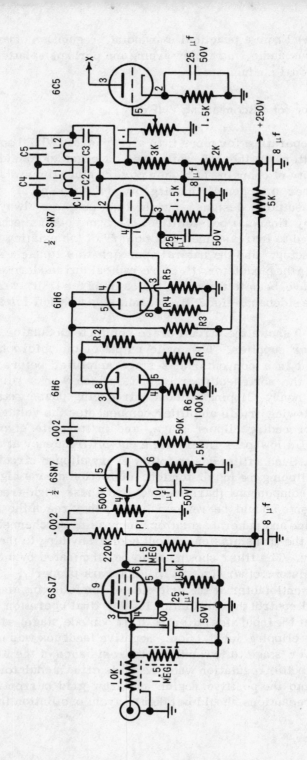

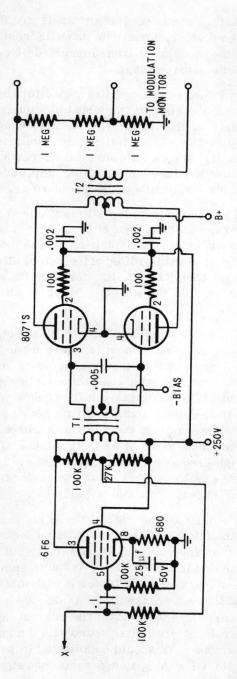

Fig. 8-9. Schematic of the "increased-talk-power" VHF man's modulator.

PARTS LIST

C1	.008 μμf 2%	
C2	.016 μμf 2%	
C3	.008 μμf 2%	
C4	.007 μμf 2%	
C5	.007 μμf 2%	
L1, L2	120 mh	

R1, R2	200K
R3, R4	200K
R5	200K
T1	Driver transformer
	turns ratio 1:3
T2	Multimatch mod. trans. 120W

121

tubes; the 100-ohm resistors at the screen terminals are for this purpose. The voltage divider, formed by three 1K resistors at the secondary of the modulation transformer, delivers about 1/3 of the total audio output voltage.

Finally, notice the low values of the coupling capacitors between the stages preceding the clipper: they should attenuate low-frequency components of the audio signal, already accentuated after the clipping process. On the other hand, the coupling blocks between the stages following the clipper are of high capacities, because here the wide flat-top amplitudes should reach the modulator stage without phase rotations.

The modulator, with a power supply for all electrodes except the plates of the 807s, was built on a 8" x 11 1/2" x 2" chassis. Be careful to avoid any hum pick-up at the input stages, as this would also appear magnified at the output after the clipping process. Resistors R1, R2, R3, R4, and R5 all should be twice the value of R6; the absolute value of all of them is not so important.

The components of the low-pass filter should be selected carefully. In my case the required capacities were made up by paralleling mica and good quality paper capacitors and selecting the proper combinations with a capacitance bridge. As inductances you can use 120-mh or 125-mh RF chokes. All these elements were mounted on a small pertinax board and then installed as a complete unit on the modulator chassis. The small capacitor between the grids of the output tubes also serves to attentuate high-frequency audio components. The modulation transformer should have adequate dimensions to take care of the marked increase in audio power.

After completing the wiring of the rig, there is not much more to do than to plug the tubes into their respective sockets and to switch on the power supply. Any transmitter with an input up to 200 watts can be modulated 100%, but with somewhat reduced voltage on the modulator plates it will just be the ideal companion unit for such transmitters as the 100-watt 6 meter rig described earlier in this book. The correct setting of the two gain controls is most easily found with the help of some sort of oscilloscope. P2 should be adjusted to permit 100% modulation with P1 wide open and some loud signal applied to the input. From then on you will not have to touch this control any more, and by varying the position of P1 you now can control the amount of clipping, increasing in this way your "talk power" without the risk of producing splatter and oversized sidebands.

CHAPTER 9

Station Listings

VHF-FM Net Directory

The purpose of the following list is to promote the selection of frequencies already in use when establishing a new network of stations with equipment formerly used in taxicabs or police cars. Wide-band FM uses fixed-frequency, crystal-controlled receivers and transmitters. Crystals are expensive, so it is very wise to make a good selection at the beginning. Once established, it is very difficult to get a net to move to another channel. Thought should be given to the selection, not only in terms of the local operation, but in light of frequencies used within reasonable driving distances since usually over half of the units are mobiles. Multifrequency operation is usually possible with simple modifications. This allows the use of 2, 3, or more frequencies within reasonable limits (280 kHz on six, 720 kHz on two) without problems of power output tube dissipation and loss of receiver sensitivity. Even though multifrequency operation is possible, it is highly suggested that the primary channels listed below be the channel with the most activity due to the roving mobile passing through your area.

We heartily suggest the use of a frequency that is already in use. For 6 meters, 52.525 MHz is by far the leader in use. It is believed that there are as many stations on this frequency as there are on all other 6 meter FM frequencies combined. It is presently used in at least 9 states and is spreading rapidly. Front end overloading of TV receivers on Channel 2 is minimized by the use of this frequency. The second choice would be a presently used channel in the RACES segment (53.35-53.75 MHz). For 2 meters, where there are few TVI problems, there are primary channels in both RACES segments. In the lower segment (145.17-145.71 MHz) the primary channel is 145.26 MHz. In the upper segment (146.79-147.33 MHz) the primary channel is 147.30 MHz. It is well worthy of note that

Technicians can operate on 145.26 MHz, since it is within their 145-147 MHz requirement. In the unlikely event of new channels being established, it is suggested that they be placed at multiples of 40 kHz on 6 meters and 60 kHz on 2 meters from the above listed primary channels. (Example: 53.60, 53.64, 145.26, 145.50) Give your frequency wide publicity. We suggest plus or minus 15-kHz deviation, as this is the amount for which the equipment was designed.

Listing of a city in CAPITAL LETTERS indicates that this frequency has more extensive amateur use in that area, whereas listing in small letters indicates that the use of the frequency in that area is more limited or for a specific purpose, such as CD nets, so-called private channels, etc.

6 Meters

FREQUENCY	LOCATION	# CALLS	LIAISON
52.525 MHz	OLD GREENWICH, CONN.	—	—
	GREATER CHICAGO, ILL.	6	W9QBH
	ANGOLA, IND.	15	K1CMT/9
	ELKHART, IND.	3	K9DOF
	FORT WAYNE, IND.	20	W9PRO
	HUNTINGTON, IND.	5	W9INV
	INDIANAPOLIS, IND.	25	W9KYU
	CEDAR RAPIDS, IOWA	—	—
	LAFAYETTE, IND.	10	W9KRE
	BATTLE CREEK, MICH.	—	K8GOQ
	BENTON HARBOR, MICH.	5	K8JMA
	KALAMAZOO, MICH.	16	K8AFJ
	GREATER ST. LOUIS, MO.	3	WØPYS
	KENTON, OHIO	2	K8ANT
	SALT LAKE CITY, UTAH	—	—
	LYNCHBURG, VA.	6	W4DYE
	RICHMOND, VA.	8	W4DXC
52.530 MHz	CLEVELAND, OHIO	7	W8AZO

52.580 MHz	SYRACUSE, N.Y.	7	K2KZL
	TROY, N.Y.	14	W2KLZ
	PROVIDENCE, R.I.	4	—
	Lynchburg, Va.	3	W4DYE
52.640 MHz	Kalamazoo, Mich.	—	K8AFJ
	Angola, Ind.	—	K1CMT/9
53.000 MHz	SAN ANTONIO, TEX.	9	W5LVE
53.098 MHz	Portland, Ore.	2	W7VS
	Seattle, Wash.	2	W7FNO
53.290 MHz	OLYMPIA, WASH.	63	W7UVH
53.440 MHz	Onondaga County, N.Y.	12	K2JIM
53.480 MHz	AUBURN, N.Y.	—	K2AJV
53.560 MHz	Milwaukee, Wisc.	8	—
53.600 MHz	LOUISVILLE, KY.	20	W4BAZ
	DUPAGE COUNTY, ILL.	—	—
	Onondaga County, N.Y.	8	K2JIM

2 Meters

Frequency	Location		Callsign
146.76 MHz	SEATTLE, WASH.	110	W7YKA
	Boise, Ida.	—	—
	COQUILLE, ORE.	—	—
	Los Angeles, Calif.	—	—
	San Diego, Calif.	—	—
146.82 MHz	Seattle, Wash.	—	W7FNO
146.88 MHz	Seattle, Wash.	—	W7FNO
146.90 MHz	QUINCY, ILL.	—	K9KCY
	Toledo, Ohio	6	K8DPE
146.94 MHz	CHICAGO, ILL. AREA	—	K9OJV
	ANNE ARUNDEL COUNTY, MD.	10	W3NAE
	Seattle, Wash.	8	W7FNO
	Milwaukee, Wisc.		—
146.97 MHz	Chicago, Ill.	3	K9OJV
	DALLAS, TEX.	—	K5MYG
146.98 MHz	ROANOKE, VA.	5	K4UMK
147.00 MHz	Milwaukee, Wisc.	6	—

Frequency	Location		
147.06 MHz	Chicago, Ill.	—	K9OJV
147.18 MHz	CHICAGO, ILL. AREA	—	K9OJV
	Pittsburgh, Pa.	48	W3UGV
	Milwaukee, Wisc.	8	—
147.24 MHz	CHICAGO SUBURBS	—	K9OJV
	Cleveland, Ohio	—	W8TR
	St. Louis, Mo.	—	—
147.30 MHz	CHICAGO, ILL. AREA	—	K9OJV
	NORTHWESTERN INDIANA	100	W9EHZ
	CENTRAL INDIANA	100	K9KRE
	LOUISVILLE, KY.	30	W4BAZ
	Detroit, Mich.	—	—
	Columbus, Ohio	1	W8RSY
	ST. LOUIS, MO.	—	—
	Cleveland, Ohio	3	W8GMS
	Anne Arundel County, Md.	3	W3NAE
	Appleton, Wisc.	—	—
	CHAMPAIGN, ILL.	—	—
147.40 MHz	Chicago, Ill.	6	K9OJV
147.50 MHz	CHICAGO, ILL.	100 +	W9LLZ

Frequency	Location		Call
147.60 MHz	Chicago, Ill.	—	K9OJV
	PORTSMOUTH, VA.	5	K4STE
147.70 MHz	Chicago, Ill.	12	K9OJV
144.70 MHz	Seattle, Wash.	—	W7FNO
145.17 MHz	Portland, Ore.	14	W7VS
145.20 MHz	State of Ohio	—	—
	San Antonio, Tex.	—	W5LVE
	Longmont, Col.	—	—
	Baltimore, Md.	—	—
	Detroit, Mich.	—	—
	Cleveland, Ohio	—	W8ITR
145.26 MHz	Lynchburg, Va.	43	W4DYE
	Syracuse, N.Y.	20	W2AMY
	Columbus, Ohio	35	W8OQT
	Worthington, Ohio	—	W8RSY
	Westerville, Ohio	—	—
	Washington, D.C.	—	W4ZAW
	Norfolk, Va.	—	—
	Amherst, Va.	—	W4MXH
	Roanoke, Va.	—	K4ZAD or K4UMK

Frequency	Location		
145.32 MHz	Cleveland, Ohio	50	W8BUQ
	Detroit, Mich.	—	—
	Ottawa County, Ohio	—	—
145.35 MHz	Baltimore, Md.	—	—
145.38 MHz	Birmingham, Ala.	12	—
	Milwaukee, Wisc.	—	—
145.44 MHz	Toledo, Ohio	50	K8DPE
145.50 MHz	Boise, Idaho	—	W7OL
145.53 MHz	Memphis, Tenn.	6	—
	Milwaukee, Wisc.	12	—
145.59 MHz	Milwaukee, Wisc.	—	—
	Utica, N.Y.	15	W2SSL
145.68 MHz	Lynchburg, Va.	43	W4DYE
	Amherst, Va.	—	W4MXH
	Roanoke, Va.	—	K4ZAD or K4UMK

UHF Station Directory

The following is a list of stations believed to be active on the amateur bands above 220 MHz. Because of the devious methods used to gather this information, no guarantee of accuracy can be made. An attempt has been made to exclude stations that may have been active at one time but who now have become inactive; however, many stations included on this list may not really classify as being active at this time. I suggest that you contact any of the stations in which you are interested.

220 MHz

Phoenix, Ariz.	W7RUX
Tucson, Ariz.	K7HID
Tucson, Ariz.	K7HJD
Tucson, Ariz.	W7AMH
Tucson, Ariz.	W7FGG
Arlington, Calif.	K6GTG
Costa Mesa, Calif.	K6IBY
Fresno, Calif.	W6BJI
La Mesa, Calif.	W6IEY
Larkspur, Calif.	W6OKR
Long Beach, Calif.	K6GKX
Los Altos, Calif.	W6ASH
Los Angeles, Calif.	W6MMU
Mill Valley, Calif.	W6NZV
Oakland, Calif.	K6RNQ
Oxnard, Calif.	K6UZC
Palos Verdes, Calif.	W6NLZ
Porterville, Calif.	W6FZA
Sonoma, Calif.	W6AJF
Sunnyvale, Calif.	K6JTC
Canton, Conn.	W1HDQ
Collinsville, Conn.	W1QVF
Elmwood, Conn.	W1HDF
Fairfield, Conn.	W1USF
Green Farms, Conn.	W1MFT
Milford, Conn.	W1OSQ
Southington, Conn.	W1FOM
Waterbury, Conn.	W1JZA

W. Hartford, Conn.	W1YDS
Wilmington, Del.	W3CGV
Jacksonville, Fla.	W4RMU
Athens, Ga.	W4UML
Auburn, Ga.	K4QAB
Decatur, Ga.	K4TFY
Doraville, Ga.	W4FWH
Hoschton, Ga.	K4KLD
Toddville, Iowa	WØOFY
Aurora, Ill.	K9MXR
Aurora, Ill.	K9ONW
Aurora, Ill.	W9EQC
Berwyn, Ill.	W9JGN
Chicago, Ill.	K9JIJ
Chicago, Ill.	K9OTE
Chicago, Ill.	W9DJ
Chicago, Ill.	W9JCS
Chicago, Ill.	W9ZIH
Downers Grove, Ill.	W9REM
Glen Ellyn, Ill.	K9DWR
Hammond, Ill.	W9OVL
Lake Zurich, Ill.	K9DOE
Lincolnwood, Ill.	W9RWQ
Naperville, Ill.	W9RPF
Norwood Park, Ill.	K9KIP
Oswego, Ill.	W9SKN
Paxton, Ill.	W9RYM
Rockford, Ill.	W9BQC
Roselle, Ill.	W9ROS
Skokie, Ill.	K9AMG
Skokie, Ill.	K9BDJ
Skokie, Ill.	W9BOD
So. Holland, Ill.	W9JEC
Wheaton, Ill.	K9HWC
Wheaton, Ill.	K9ILH
Woodhull, Ill.	W9AAG
E. Chicago, Ind.	W9WOY

Griffith, Ind.	W9VVH
Huntertown, Ind.	K9CXV
Indianapolis, Ind.	W9JIY
Portland, Ind.	W9ULH
Valpariso, Ind.	K9AQP
Kansas City, Kan.	KØJZL
Kansas City, Kan.	WØITO
Overland, Kan.	WØYZZ
Prairie Village, Kan.	KØITF
Auburn, Me.	K1CXX
So. Portland, Me.	W1WAS
Catonsville, Md.	W3ZRF
College Park, Md.	W3JZI
Greenbelt, Md.	K3CEZ
Kensington, Md.	W3LCC
Rockville, Md.	W3UJG
Silver Springs, Md.	W3AHQ
Arlington, Mass.	W1CTW
Arlington, Mass.	W1QXX
Feeding Hills, Mass.	W1VNH
Harvard, Mass.	K1JIX
Marlboro, Mass.	K1IZM
Needham, Mass.	W1OOP
Plymouth, Mass.	K1AII
Wilbraham, Mass.	W1RFU
Battle Creek, Mich.	W8PYQ
Benton Harbor, Mich.	W8PT
Detroit, Mich.	W8DX
Detroit, Mich.	W8VIX
Grand Rapids, Mich.	W8NOH
Kalamazoo, Mich.	W8CVQ
Kalamazoo, Mich.	W8GOV
Kalamazoo, Mich.	W8KSZ
Ostimo, Mich.	K8JZR
Marks, Miss.	W6AJF
Belton, Mo.	KØTZN

Belton, Mo.	WØLRC
Jennings, Mo.	WØIFC
Raytown, Mo.	KØDGU
Roscoe, Mo.	WØDDX
Omaha, Neb.	WØYZV
Las Vegas, Nev.	K7ICW
Parker, Nev.	W7LEE
Chichester, N.H.	W1AZK
Farmington, N.H.	W1FZ
Goffstown, N.H.	W1HMT
Goshen, N.H.	W1IQD
Manchester, N.H.	K1API
Manchester, N.H.	K1CIG
Manchester, N.H.	W1PZU
Manchester, N.H.	W1WYZ
Bloomingdale, N.J.	W2PEZ
Edison, N.J.	K2JLN
Edison, N.J.	W2MGF
Elizabeth, N.J.	W2DWJ
Elizabeth, N.J.	K2PPZ
Haddonfield, N.J.	W2KFC
Livingston, N.J.	K2PCG
Manville, N.J.	K2VDK
Newark, N.J.	K2KIB
Oaklyn, N.J.	K2SMZ
Packanack Lake, N.J.	K2LYR
Passaic, N.J.	K2QWE
Plainfield, N.J.	K2RMD
Rahway, N.J.	K2DZM
Rahway, N.J.	W2SHU
Rivervale, N.J.	K2AXQ
Roseland, N.J.	W2BVJ
Saddle River, N.J.	W2NTY
Somerville, N.J.	K2RIA
Somerville, N.J.	W2SLZ
So. Plainfield, N.J.	W2AGK
So. Plainfield, N.J.	W2SMJ
Teaneck, N.J.	W2DZA

Tenafly, N.J.	K2DIG
Union, N.J.	WA2DEC
Warrenville, N.J.	W2JDU
Wayne, N.J.	K2HAZ
Albuquerque, N.M.	K5WGF
Albuquerque, N.M.	W5BFH
Socorro, N.M.	K5UNK
Bellport, N.Y.	W2LRJ
Brooklyn, N.Y.	W2AOC
Buffalo, N.Y.	K2GUG
Ellicottville, N.Y.	W2EJO
Freeport, N.Y.	W2SEU
Glen Head, N.Y.	W2WOF
Little Neck, N.Y.	W2HVL
Mt. Vernon, N.Y.	W2HBC
N. Syracuse, N.Y.	K2GGA
New Rochelle, N.Y.	K2BVC
Orangeburg, N.Y.	K2HIL
Patchogue, N.Y.	K2QJQ
Plattsburgh, N.Y.	K2MEB
Port Washington, N.Y.	W2LBK
Rhinebeck, N.Y.	W2LKP
Troy, N.Y.	K2CBA
Troy, N.Y.	K2ISA
Wappingers Falls, N.Y.	W2LWI
Greensboro, N.C.	W4ZXI
Kanuku, Oahu	KH6UK
Cincinnati, Ohio	K8PUT
Cincinnati, Ohio	W8LPD
Columbus, Ohio	W8BAX
Columbus, Ohio	W8WRN
Dayton, Ohio	W8BMO
Dayton, Ohio	W8NEE
Fairborn, Ohio	W8SVI
Hubbard, Ohio	W8SFG
Lakewood, Ohio	W8NRM
Powell, Ohio	W8CSW
Summit Station, Ohio	W8LGI
Tipp City, Ohio	W8GHX

Waynesville, Ohio	W8ZCV
W. Richfield, Ohio	W8IJG
Youngstown, Ohio	W8SZN
Youngstown, Ohio	W8VIY
Toronto, Ont.	VE3AIB
Toronto, Ont.	VE3BQN
Portland, Ore.	W7HBH
Allentown, Pa.	W3BPZ
Allentown, Pa.	W3BYF
Bareville, Pa.	K3HQC
Belle Vernon, Pa.	W3RUE
Bradford, Pa.	K3BBO
Bradford, Pa.	W3ZFA
Carnegie, Pa.	W3ANX
Doylestown, Pa.	K3BPP
E. Berlin, Pa.	W3AJD
E. Petersburg, Pa.	W3JYL
Fleetwood, Pa.	W3SNM
Hanover, Pa.	W3MUM
Havertown, Pa.	W3HFY
Johnstown, Pa.	W3TIF
Lancaster, Pa.	W3FEY
Lewisberry, Pa.	W3CAJ
Palmyra, Pa.	W3ATL
Philadelphia, Pa.	K3IUV
Philadelphia, Pa.	W3ZRR
Quakertown, Pa.	W3HIX
Scranton, Pa.	W3ARW
Scranton, Pa.	W3LZD
Willow Grove, Pa.	W3KKN
Willow Grove, Pa.	W3VIR
York, Pa.	K2AAX
York, Pa.	W3BJG
York, Pa.	W3HZU
York, Pa.	W3QFM
Middletown, R.I.	W1AJR
Tiverton, R.I.	W1UHE
Greenville, S.C.	W4TLC
Greenville, S.C.	W4VIW

Nashville, Tenn.	W4RFR
Oak Ridge, Tenn.	W4VSN
Arlington, Texas	K5BDD
Dallas, Texas	W5AJG
Danville, Vermont	W1EXZ
Alexandria, Va.	K4RAY
Annandale, Va.	W4UBY
Fairfax, Va.	W4SEQ
Falls Church, Va.	K4TFU
Falls Church, Va.	W4UMF
Woodbridge, Va.	K4UKQ
Seattle, Wash.	W7RT
Elkins, W. Va.	K8AXU
Wheeling, W. Va.	K8AOM
Milwaukee, Wisc.	W9JFP

432 MHz

Demopolis, Ala.	W4TLV
Gurdon, Ark.	W5JWL
Phoenix, Ariz.	W7RUX
Arcadia, Calif.	WA6BFC
Berkeley, Calif.	K6GWE
Camarillo, Calif.	W6HPH
Costa Mesa, Calif.	K6IBY
Highlands, Calif.	W6GTG
Larkspur, Calif.	W6OKR
Oakland, Calif.	W6OHQ
Oxnard, Calif.	W6SDM
Palos Verdes Estates, Calif.	W6NLZ
Sacramento, Calif.	W6PIV
San Jose, Calif.	K6HCP
Sonoma, Calif.	W6AJF

Taft, Calif.	W6BUT
Turlock, Calif.	W6NTV
Elmwood, Conn.	W1HDF
Green Farms, Conn.	W1MFT
Niantic, Conn.	W1ZPV
Newark, Del.	W3RWT
Newark, Del.	W3WHZ
Wilmington, Del.	W3CGV
Chamblee, Ga.	W4BSJ
Chicago, Ill.	W9AGM
Chicago, Ill.	W9ALE
Chicago, Ill.	W9AYM
Chicago, Ill.	W9FHS
Chicago, Ill.	W9ITL
Chicago, Ill.	W9KKU
Chicago, Ill.	W9LX
Chicago, Ill.	W9OKB
Chicago, Ill.	W9PBP
Chicago, Ill.	W9PVO
Chicago, Ill.	W9PWH
Chicago, Ill.	W9QVO
Chicago, Ill.	W9SQE
Chicago, Ill.	W9ZIH
Des Plaines, Ill.	W9DRN
Wheaton, Ill.	W9OJI
Woodhull, Ill.	W9AAG
Iowa City, Iowa	WØDEN
Prairie Village, Kan.	KØITF
Glendale, Ky.	W4HJQ
Shreveport, La.	W5KTD
So. Portland, Me.	W1WAS
Kensington, Md.	W3LCC
Pleasant Hill, Md.	W3GGR
Rockville, Md.	W3UJG

Salisbury, Md.	W3BSV
Silver Springs, Md.	W3RE
Danvers, Mass.	W1IO
Feeding Hills, Mass.	W1VNH
Harvard, Mass.	K1JIX
Needham, Mass.	W1OOP
Benton Harbor, Mich.	W8PT
Berkley, Mich.	W8IPR
Detroit, Mich.	K8AIY
Detroit, Mich.	W8ARR
Detroit, Mich.	W8DX
Detroit, Mich.	W8HBB
Detroit, Mich.	W8HRC
Inkster, Mich.	W8UCT
Livonia, Mich.	W8RLT
Plymouth, Mich.	W8TWT
Saginaw, Mich.	W8PQO
Marks, Miss.	W5RCI
Farmington, N.H.	K1NXI
Farmington, N.H.	W1FZ
Bergenfield, N.J.	W2BQK
Bernardsville, N.J.	W2KDZ
Bloomfield, N.J.	W2VYF
Elizabeth, N.J.	W2DWJ
Haddon Heights, N.J.	W2BLV
Newark, N.J.	K2KIB
Parlin, N.J.	K2UUR
Pennington, N.J.	W2VCG
Rahway, N.J.	K2DZM
Rochelle Park, N.J.	W2NTY
Somerville, N.J.	K2HAC
Teaneck, N.J.	W2DZA
Tenafly, N.J.	K2DIG
Woodstown, N.J.	W2FQK
Woodstown, N.J.	W2HEK
Babylon, N.Y.	W2SCG

Baldwin, N.Y.	K2AZT
Bellport, N.Y.	W2LRJ
Elmhurst, N.Y.	W2VSA
Flushing, N.Y.	W2AOD
Glen Head, N.Y.	W2WOF
Hicksville, N.Y.	K2ASI
Mt. Vernon, N.Y.	W2HBC
Porter Corners, N.Y.	K2GRI
Richmond Hill, N.Y.	W2PPT
Troy, N.Y.	K2CBA
Troy, N.Y.	K2ISA
Wantagh, N.Y.	W2OTA
Kanuku, Oahu	KH6UK
Columbus, Ohio	K8AGO
Columbus, Ohio	W8BAX
Columbus, Ohio	W8DMR
Columbus, Ohio	W8TYY
Dayton, Ohio	W8GVG
Dayton, Ohio	W8HTD
Lakewood, Ohio	W8NRM
Port Clinton, Ohio	W8UB
Sandusky, Ohio	W8HCC
Toledo, Ohio	W8JLQ
Toledo, Ohio	W8RQI
Toledo, Ohio	W8TTY
Toledo, Ohio	W8UST
Toledo, Ohio	W8VCO
Van Buren, Ohio	W8VOZ
Wewoka, Okla.	W5HTZ
Corvallis, Ore.	K7JSJ
Portland, Ore.	W7HBH
Belle Vernon, Pa.	W3RUE
Bethlehem, Pa.	W3JNC
Bethlehem, Pa.	W3SAP
Dallastown, Pa.	W3CRL
E. Berlin, Pa.	W3AJD
Lancaster, Pa.	W3FEY

Levittown, Pa.	K3EH
Penndel, Pa.	K3EOF
Perkasie, Pa.	W3IMW
Perkasie, Pa.	W3IVL
Philadelphia, Pa.	W3FLX
Scranton, Pa.	W3ARW
Sellersville, Pa.	W3MAG
Willow Grove, Pa.	W3VIR
York, Pa.	K3AAX
York, Pa.	W3MMW
York, Pa.	W3SST
Middletown, R.I.	W1AJR
Tiverton, R.I.	W1UHE
Collierville, Tenn.	W4HHK
Nashville, Tenn.	W4RFR
Dallas, Texas	W5AJG
Hampton, Va.	K4ALH
Hampton, Va.	W4SCJ
Newport News, Va.	W4NRB
Norfolk, Va.	W4ZVX
Phoebus, Va.	W4VVE
Kirkland, Wash.	W7IHL
Yakima, Wash.	K7GGJ
Beloit, Wisc.	W9GAB

1215 MHz

Canton, Conn.	W1HDQ
Granby, Conn.	K1CJX
W. Hartford, Conn.	W1CUT
Feeding Hills, Mass.	W1VNH
Springfield, Mass.	W1QWJ
Springfield, Mass.	W1RVW
Springfield, Mass.	W1STR

Wilbraham, Mass.	W1WFL
Wilbraham, Mass.	W1YDS

1296 MHz

Camarillo, Calif.	W6HPH
La Cresenta, Calif.	W6JRK
Long Beach, Calif.	W6SSB
Los Angeles, Calif.	W6MMU
Menlo Park, Calif.	W6HB
Palos Verdes Estates, Calif.	W6NLZ
Panorama City, Calif.	W6HIT
Richmond, Calif.	K6AXN
Rivera, Calif.	W6DQJ
San Diego, Calif.	W6BLK
Santa Monica, Calif.	W6PCQ
Wilmington, Del.	W3CGV
Pleasant Hill, Md.	W3GGR
Medfield, Mass.	W1BU
Needham, Mass.	W1OOP
Pluckemin, N.J.	K2TKN
Porter Corners, N.Y.	K2GRI
Troy, N.Y.	K2CBA
Troy, N.Y.	K2ISA
Dorset, Ohio	W8LIO
Lancaster, Pa.	W3FEY
Scranton, Pa.	W3ARW

CHAPTER 10

VHF Construction Projects

The projects which follow have been compiled for the advanced VHF enthusiast capable of constructing tube and semiconductor units with no further instruction than the basic schematic diagram. In short, these are not for the rank beginner as starter projects. Novices should follow those items presented in detail in earlier chapters.

A few words about these circuits. First, they are all inexpensive to construct, and should work on the first go-around. Precautions, however, should be observed—particularly wiring techniques. As with all VHF projects, wiring should be short and to the point. Where possible, there should be no wiring at all, save resistor leads, etc. Even the shortest of wires can become inductive at the higher frequencies; a difference in trimming lead length of only 1/8" can severely affect performance of the finished unit. Exercise care—and proven VHF/UHF construction techniques—and you'll be using these gadgets inside of an evening.

Experiment — Modify

For the advanced enthusiast, bear in mind that recommended component values are for the most part flexible. If you're fairly knowledgable in VHF construction, you should have no trouble putting together working units, using the diagrams merely as guidelines. Few are absolutely critical. For example, if the parts list calls for a capacitor value of "26 pfd var.," there's nothing to prevent your using a 25 pfd variable, a 30 pfd variable, or even a 35 pfd variable—providing we're not, say, at 1296 MHz where such a value would be critical. Use your own common VHF horsesense, and you're on your way!

. . . for 50 MHz

50 db Six Meter Preamp

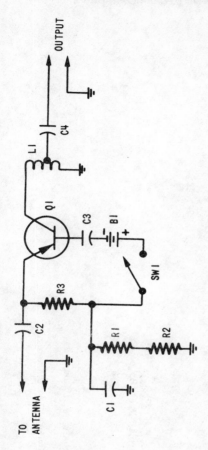

PARTS LIST

Q1 — Philco T2028
C1, 2, 3 — .0047 mfd
C4 — 16 pfd
R1 — 5.7K
R2 — 28K
R3 — 1.1K
L1 — Coil made to resonate at 50 MHz, with C4 tapped 1/3 of length from cold end.
SW1 — SPST Oak Type 200 or equiv.
B1 — 12v DC

14-watt 50-MHz Linear Amplifier

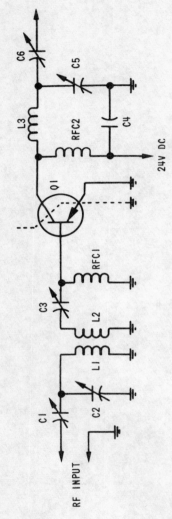

RF INPUT

24V DC

PARTS LIST

Q1 — Choose from any of Motorola's line of HF power
        transistors.

C1 — 51 pfd var.

C2, 3, 5, 6 — 31 pfd var.

C4 — .022 mfd

L1, 2 — 4 turns of #16 enameled wire, 1" diameter,
        1/2" long.

L3 — 3 turns of #12 enameled wire, 1 1/4" diameter,
        3/8" long.

RFC1 — Ohmite Z-50
RFC2 — Ohmite Z-460

Inexpensive 50-MHz Receiver

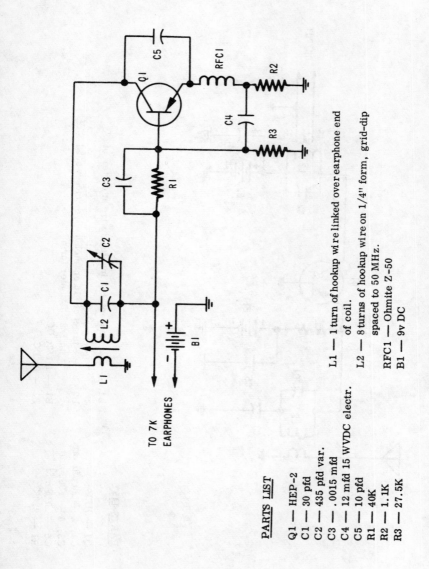

L1 — 1 turn of hookup wire linked over earphone end of coil.

L2 — 8 turns of hookup wire on 1/4" form, grid-dip spaced to 50 MHz.

RFC1 — Ohmite Z-50

B1 — 9v DC

PARTS LIST

Q1 — HEP-2
C1 — 30 pfd
C2 — 435 pfd var.
C3 — .0015 mfd
C4 — 12 mfd 15 WVDC electr.
C5 — 10 pfd
R1 — 40K
R2 — 1.1K
R3 — 27.5K

50-MHz Preamp

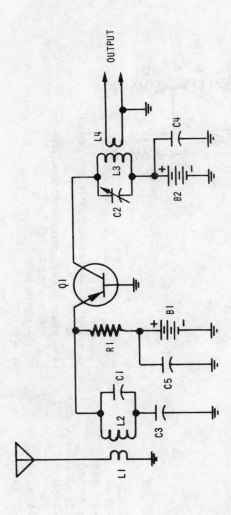

PARTS LIST

Q1 — HEP-2
C1, 2 — 30 pfd var.
C3, 4 — .002 mfd
C5 — .015 mfd
R1 — 2.6K

L1, 4 — 2 turns of #20 insulated wire at center of L2, L3.
L2, 3 — 8 turns of #16 enameled wire, closewound on 1/2" diameter form.
B1 — 1 1/2v DC
B2 — 9v DC

Tunnel Diode Transmitter

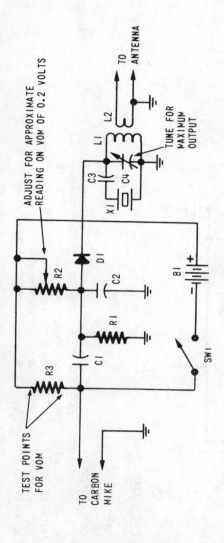

ADJUST FOR APPROXIMATE
READING ON VOM OF 0.2 VOLTS

TO ANTENNA

TUNE FOR MAXIMUM OUTPUT

L2

L1

C3

C4

X1

D1

R2

C2

R1

C1

R3

B1

+

−

SW1

TEST POINTS FOR VOM

TO CARBON MIKE

PARTS LIST

D1 — XA-653 tunnel diode
C1 — 2 mfd
C2 — .0015 mfd
C3 — 35 pfd
C4 — 51 pfd var.
R1 — 11
R2 — 75 pot.
R3 — 102

L1 — 4 turns #16 enameled wire spaced to 5/8" on a 5/8" diameter coil form.
L2 — 2 turns of #16 enameled wire wound over center of L1.
X1 — 25-MHz crystal
SW1 — SPST
B1 — 1.35v DC hearing-aid mercury battery

Flea-Power Rig

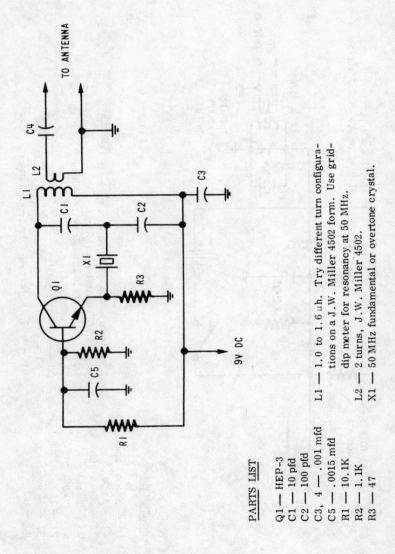

TO ANTENNA

L1 — 1.0 to 1.6 μh. Try different turn configurations on a J.W. Miller 4502 form. Use grid-dip meter for resonancy at 50 MHz.

L2 — 2 turns, J.W. Miller 4502.

X1 — 50 MHz fundamental or overtone crystal.

PARTS LIST

Q1 — HEP-3
C1 — 10 pfd
C2 — 100 pfd
C3, 4 — .001 mfd
C5 — .0015 mfd
R1 — 10.1K
R2 — 1.1K
R3 — 47

One-Tube Phone Transmitter

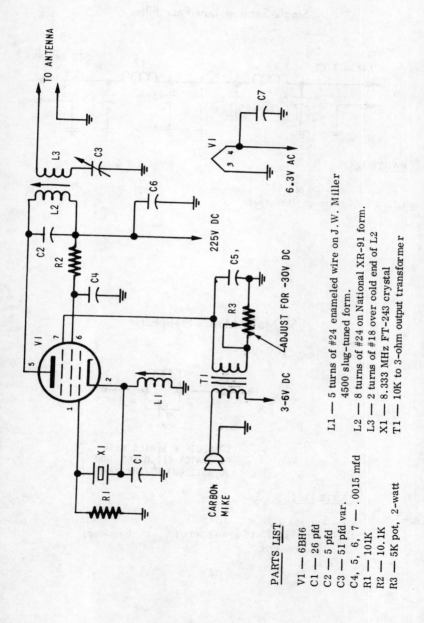

PARATS LIST

V1 — 6BH6
C1 — 26 pfd
C2 — 5 pfd
C3 — 51 pfd var.
C4, 5, 6, 7 — .0015 mfd
R1 — 101K
R2 — 10.1K
R3 — 5K pot, 2-watt

L1 — 5 turns of #24 enameled wire on J.W. Miller 4500 slug-tuned form.
L2 — 8 turns of #24 on National XR-91 form.
L3 — 2 turns of #18 over cold end of L2
X1 — 8.333 MHz FT-243 crystal
T1 — 10K to 3-ohm output transformer

Single-Section Low-Pass Filter

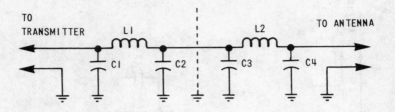

PARTS <u>LIST</u>

C1, 2, 3, 4 — 60 pfd
L1, 2 — 4 turns of B&W 3002

Six Meter Mobile Hash Filter

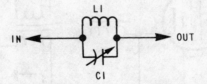

CONNECT IN SERIES WITH
GENERATOR FIELD AND TUNE
TO NULL OUT 50-MHz HASH

PARTS <u>LIST</u>

C1 — 30 pfd var.
L1 — 5 turns of #10 enameled wire, 1" diameter,
     closewound.

One-Nuvistor Preselector

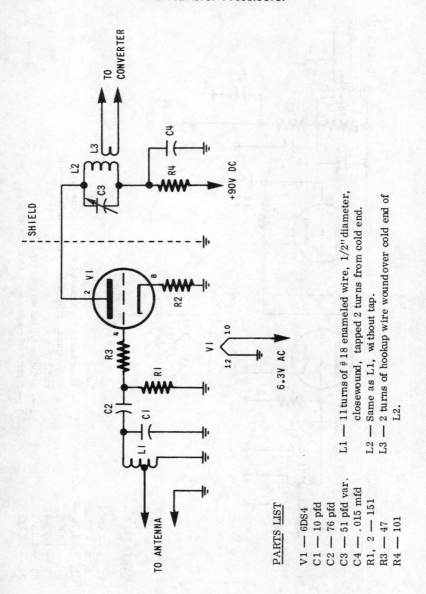

PARTS LIST

V1 — 6DS4
C1 — 10 pfd
C2 — 76 pfd
C3 — 51 pfd var.
C4 — .015 mfd
R1, 2 — 151
R3 — 47
R4 — 101

L1 — 11 turns of #18 enameled wire, 1/2" diameter, closewound, tapped 2 turns from cold end.
L2 — Same as L1, without tap.
L3 — 2 turns of hookup wire wound over cold end of L2.

Two-Nuvistor Preselecter

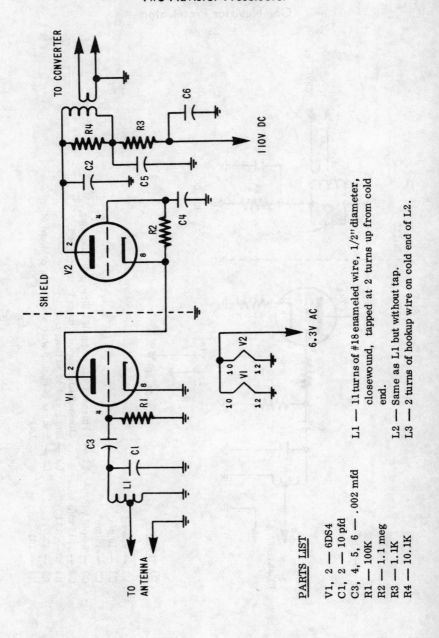

TO CONVERTER

110V DC

SHIELD

6.3V AC

TO ANTENNA

L1 — 11 turns of #18 enameled wire, 1/2" diameter, closewound, tapped at 2 turns up from cold end.

L2 — Same as L1 but without tap.

L3 — 2 turns of hookup wire on cold end of L2.

PARTS LIST

V1, 2 — 6DS4
C1, 2 — 10 pfd
C3, 4, 5, 6 — .002 mfd
R1 — 100K
R2 — 1.1 meg
R3 — 1.1K
R4 — 10.1K

. . . for 144 MHz

Superregenerative Receiver

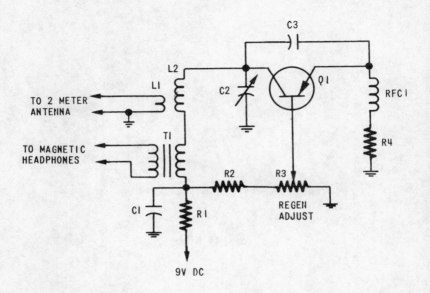

PARTS LIST

Q1 — GE-9
C1 — .0015 mfd
C2, 3 — 12 pfd var.
R1 — 10K
R2 — 47K
R3 — 25K pot
R4 — 2.1K
L1 — 2-turn link over center of L2.
L2 — 4 turns of #16 enameled wire, closewound on
5/16" diameter coil form.
T1 — Audio transformer: 2K primary, 10K secon-
dary.
RFC1 — Z-144 (Ohmite)

144-MHz Transmitter

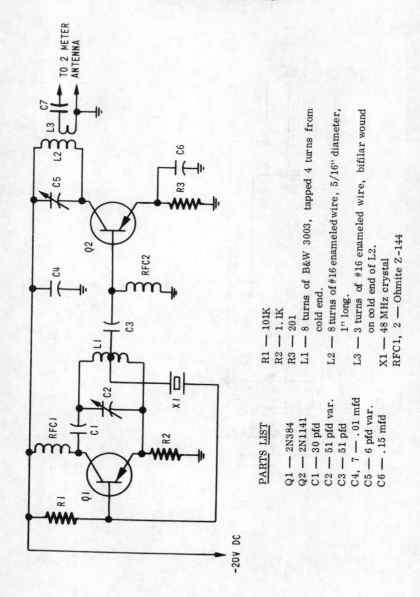

TO 2 METER ANTENNA

−20V DC

PARTS LIST

Q1 — 2N384
Q2 — 2N1141
C1 — 30 pfd
C2 — 51 pfd var.
C3 — 51 pfd
C4, 7 — .01 mfd
C5 — 6 pfd var.
C6 — .15 mfd

R1 — 101K
R2 — 1.1K
R3 — 201
L1 — 8 turns of B&W 3003, tapped 4 turns from cold end.
L2 — 8 turns of #16 enameled wire, 5/16" diameter, 1" long.
L3 — 3 turns of #16 enameled wire, bifilar wound on cold end of L2.
X1 — 48 MHz crystal
RFC1, 2 — Ohmite Z-144

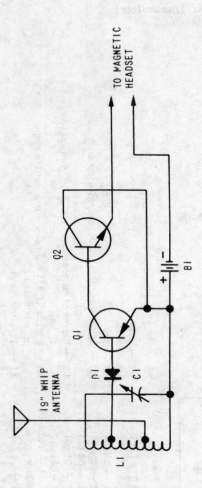

19" WHIP ANTENNA

TO MAGNETIC HEADSET

Q1

Q2

D1

C1

L1

B1

Simple 144-MHz Receiver

PARTS LIST

Q1 — GE-2
Q2 — GE-8
D1 — 1N82A
C1 — 6 pfd var.
L1 — 4 turns of #16 tinned, 3/4" diameter form,
      1/2" long. Antenna tap is 1/2-turn from top.
      Diode tap is 2 turns up from bottom.

B1 — 3v DC

160

Nuvistor Preselector

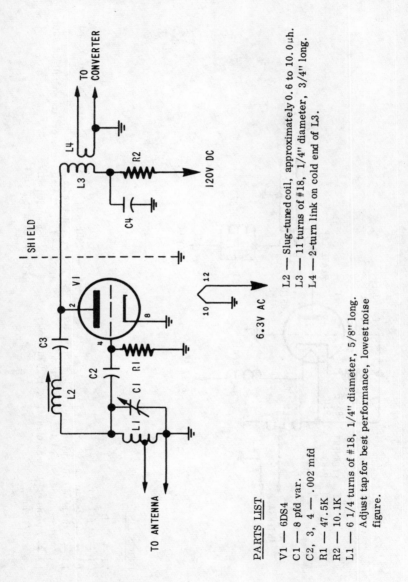

L2 — Slug-tuned coil, approximately 0.6 to 10.0 μh.
L3 — 11 turns of #18, 1/4" diameter, 3/4" long.
L4 — 2-turn link on cold end of L3.

PARTS LIST

V1 — 6DS4
C1 — 8 pfd var.
C2, 3, 4 — .002 mfd
R1 — 47.5K
R2 — 10.1K
L1 — 6 1/4 turns of #18, 1/4" diameter, 5/8" long.
    Adjust tap for best performance, lowest noise
    figure.

416B Preamplifier

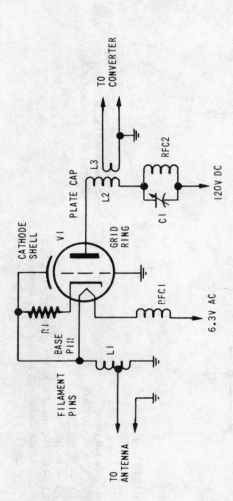

PARTS LIST

V1 — 416B

C1 — 51 pfd var.

R1 — 40, 2-watt

L1 — 4 turns of #16 enameled wire, 3/8"diameter, closewound. Tap 1 1/2 turns from top.

L2 — 7 turns of #16 enameled wire, 1/2" diameter, 3/4" long.

L3 — 2 turns of #20 insulated wire, wound around cold end of L2.

RFC1 — 471, 2-watt resistor wound full of #30 enameled wire.

RFC2 — Ohmite Z-144

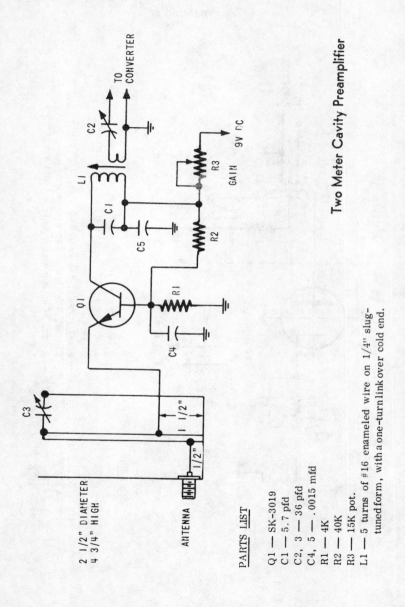

2 1/2" DIAMETER
4 3/4" HIGH

ANTENNA

TO CONVERTER

9V DC

GAIN

1 1/2"

1/2"

C3

C2

L1

C1

C5

Q1

R1

R2

R3

C4

Two Meter Cavity Preamplifier

PARTS LIST

Q1 — SK-3019
C1 — 5.7 pfd
C2, 3 — 36 pfd
C4, 5 — .0015 mfd
R1 — 4K
R2 — 40K
R3 — 15K pot.
L1 — 5 turns of #16 enameled wire on 1/4" slug-tuned form, with a one-turn link over cold end.

417A Preamplifier

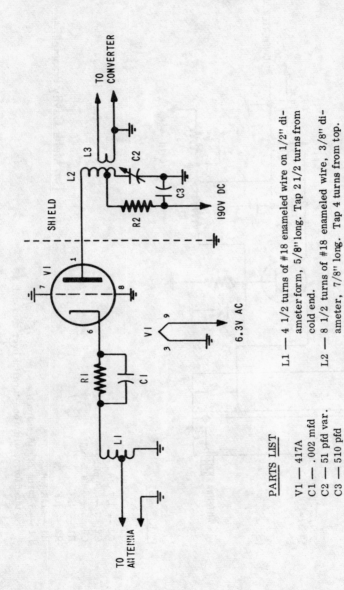

L1 — 4 1/2 turns of #18 enameled wire on 1/2" diameter form, 5/8" long. Tap 2 1/2 turns from
cold end.

L2 — 8 1/2 turns of #18 enameled wire, 3/8" diameter, 7/8" long. Tap 4 turns from top.

L3 — 2 turns of hookup wire linked over cold end of
L2.

<u>PARTS LIST</u>

V1 — 417A
C1 — .002 mfd
C2 — 51 pfd var.
C3 — 510 pfd
R1 — 72
R2 — 1.1K

. . . for 220 MHz

220-MHz Preamplifier

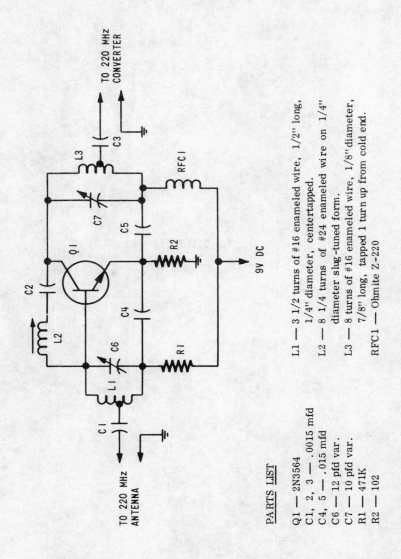

TO 220 MHz CONVERTER

TO 220 MHz ANTENNA

9V DC

PARTS LIST

Q1 — 2N3564
C1, 2, 3 — .0015 mfd
C4, 5 — .015 mfd
C6 — 12 pfd var.
C7 — 10 pfd var.
R1 — 471K
R2 — 102

L1 — 3 1/2 turns of #16 enameled wire, 1/2" long, 1/4" diameter, centertapped.
L2 — 8 1/4 turns of #24 enameled wire on 1/4" diameter slug-tuned form.
L3 — 8 turns of #16 enameled wire, 1/8" diameter, 7/8" long, tapped 1 turn up from cold end.
RFC1 — Ohmite Z-220

. . . for 432 MHz

432-MHz Preamplifier

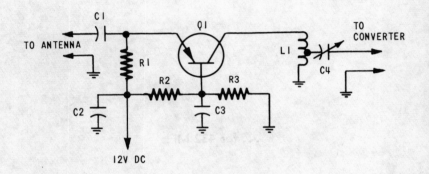

PARTS LIST

Q1 — T2020
C1 — 471 pfd
C2 — 1500 pfd
C3 — 1000 pfd
C4 — 4 pfd var.
R1 — 1.1K
R2 — 5.7K
R3 — 27.5K
L1 — 3 turns #20, 1/4" diameter, 3/4" long. Tapped 1 turn from top.

. . . for 1296 MHz

Two-Transistor Oscillator

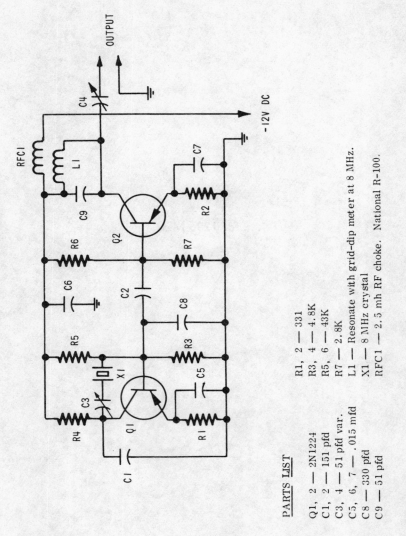

PARTS LIST

Q1, 2 — 2N1224
C1, 2 — 151 pfd
C3, 4 — 51 pfd var.
C5, 6, 7 — .015 mfd
C8 — 330 pfd
C9 — 51 pfd

R1, 2 — 331
R3, 4 — 4.8K
R5, 6 — 43K
R7 — 2.8K
L1 — Resonate with grid-dip meter at 8 MHz.
X1 — 8 MHz crystal
RFC1 — 2.5 mh RF choke. National R-100.

1296-MHz Oscillator

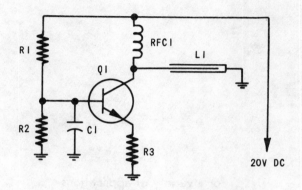

PARTS LIST

Q1 — HEP-56
C1 — 51 pfd
R1, 2 — 12.1K
R3 — 1.1K
L1 — tuned line.

. . . for a variety of applications

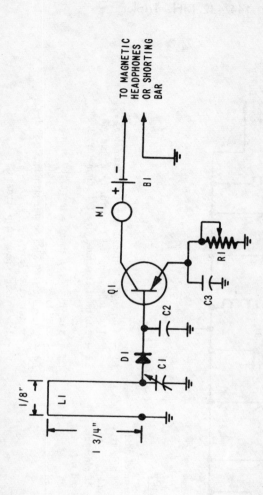

TO MAGNETIC
HEADPHONES
OR SHORTING
BAR

Field Strength Meter for 144, 220, and 432 MHz

PARTS LIST

Q1 — GE-8
D1 — 1N90
C1 — 76 pfd var.
C2 — 471 pfd
C3 — 12 mfd, 6 WVDC electr.
R1 — 2.5K pot.
L1 — Loop constructed of 5/8'' brass strip, per
     diagram.
B1 — 1 1/2v DC
M1 — 0-500 DC microammeter

144/432 MHz Tripler

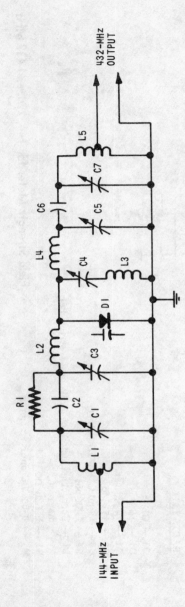

144-MHz INPUT

432-MHz OUTPUT

PARTS LIST

D1 — Varactor diode
C1, 3 — 26 pfd var.
C2 — 5 pfd
C4, 7 — 16 pfd var.
C5 — 11 pfd var.
C6 — 1 pfd.
R1 — 33.5K

L1 — 4 turns of #18 tinned wire, 1/4" diameter, 1/2" long, tapped 1 1/2 turns from cold end.
L2 — 4 turns of #18 tinned wire 1/4" diameter, 1/2" long.
L3 — 3 turns of #14 tinned wire 3/16" diameter, 3/8" long.
L4 — 2 turns of 1/8" wide copper striping, 3/8" diameter, 1/2" long.
L5 — 1 1/2" long copper strip across C1.

BC Receiver Wavetrap

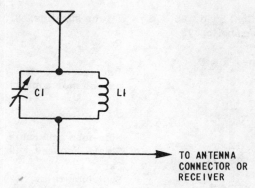

TO ANTENNA
CONNECTOR OR
RECEIVER

PARTS LIST

C1 — 27 pfd var.
L1 — 3 turns of #24 enameled wire, 1" diameter,
      1/2" long.

VHF/UHF Homebrew Noise Generator

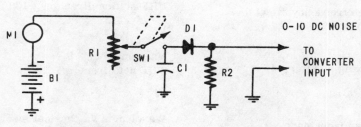

0-10 DC NOISE

TO
CONVERTER
INPUT

PARTS LIST

R2 — 56

D1 — 1N22   SW1 — SPST on R1
C1 — .001 mfd   B1 — 3v DC
R1 — 10K pot.   M1 — 0-1 DC milliammeter

INDEX